Level

7

Opening Doors

Reading and Writing Activity Book

www.santillanausa.com

Santillana USA
www.santillanausa.com

© 2007 Santillana USA Publishing Company, Inc.
2105 NW 86th Avenue
Miami, FL 33122

Opening Doors, Level 7
ISBN 10: 1-59437-309-4
ISBN 13: 978-1-59437-309-1

Art: Bill Dickson – Contact Jupiter
Layout and cover design: Noreen T. Shimano

10 09 08   6 7 8 9 10 11 12

Printed by HCI Printing and Publishing, Inc.

Santillana USA
www.santillanausa.com

Our mission is to make learning and teaching English and
Spanish an experience that is motivating, enriching, and
effective for both teachers and students. Our goal is to satisfy
the diverse needs of our customers. By involving authors,
editors, teachers and students, we produce innovative and
pedagogically sound materials that make use of the latest
technological advances. We help to develop people's
creativity. We bring ideas and imagination into education.

CONTENTS

Name _____   Date _____

a Pronouns

━━ ━━ ━━ ━━ ━━ ━━ ━━ ━━ ━━ ━━ ━━ ━━ ━━ ━━ ━━ ━━ ━━ ━━ ━━

✔ A pronoun takes the place of a noun. When using pronouns, it is important to be sure to refer to the correct person and the correct number of people or objects.

━━ ━━ ━━ ━━ ━━ ━━ ━━ ━━ ━━ ━━ ━━ ━━ ━━ ━━ ━━ ━━ ━━ ━━ ━━

■ Rewrite the following sentences using pronouns for the underlined nouns.

1. Maria is from Mexico. _____

2. Mexico is a country. _____

3. Jorge is a soccer player. _____

4. Maria and Jorge are brother and sister. _____

5. Jorge's soccer team has won all its games. _____

6. Mother was born in Mexico. _____

7. Canada is our neighbor to the north. _____

8. Lidia wants to travel to the South next year. _____

9. Paula and I took science together in middle school.

   _____

10. Mr. Gomez is my favorite teacher ever. _____

━━ ━━ ━━ ━━ ━━ ━━ ━━ ━━ ━━ ━━ ━━ ━━ ━━ ━━ ━━ ━━ ━━ ━━ ━━

■ Write five sentences about your classmates or family using pronouns.

1. _____

2. _____

3. _____

4. _____

5. _____

ELD Standard
   Identify and use parts of speech.
ELA Standard
   Make clear references between pronouns and antecedents.

Name _____   Date _____

b Capitalization and Punctuation

✓ Proper nouns are capitalized because they name a specific person or place. The names of countries are specific places and should always be capitalized.

■ Read the words below and capitalize the names of all proper nouns, writing them in the box provided below. Then write ten more proper nouns on the lines at the bottom of the page.

teacher	soccer team	honduras
middle school	friend	washington
argentina	georgia	pennsylvania avenue
georgetown	student	union street
virginia	avenue	

Proper Nouns

_____   _____
_____   _____
_____   _____
_____   _____

_____   _____
_____   _____
_____   _____
_____   _____
_____   _____

ELD Standard
    Produce independent writing with consistent use of capitalization and periods, and correct spelling.
ELA Standard
    Use correct capitalization.

Name _____   Date _____

a Pronouns

✔ A pronoun takes the place of a noun. When using pronouns, it is important to be sure you are talking about the right person and the right number of people or objects.

■ Replace each underlined noun with a pronoun and rewrite the sentences on the lines.

1. The globe is on the right side of the classroom.

   _____

2. The students are working on their science projects.

   _____

3. The book and pencil are on the desk.

   _____

4. Mr. Sales, the teacher, is explaining the project to his students.

   _____

5. Mexico and the United States are neighbors.

   _____

6. The girl is wearing a blue shirt and blue pants.

   _____

7. The middle school is right down the street.

   _____

8. Ronald has been working hard in school all year.

   _____

9. My father works for City Hall.

   _____

10. Aunt Helen will be our guest for Thanksgiving.

    _____

ELD Standard
   Identify and use parts of speech.
ELA Standard
   Make clear references between pronouns and antecedents.

3

Name _____   Date _____

b Using Quotation Marks

✔ When you want to show that someone is speaking, you use quotation marks. A comma is also added before the quotation marks.

   Example: Marta told her teacher I forgot to do my homework.

   Corrected: <u>Marta told her teacher, "I forgot to do my homework."</u>

✔ If a sentence begins with quotation marks, a comma is added at the end of the quotation.

   Example: I forgot to do my homework Maria told her teacher.

   Corrected: <u>"I forgot to do my homework," Maria told her teacher.</u>

■ Add quotation marks around the words that are spoken by each individual. Be sure to put a comma in the correct place.

1. I will read the next paragraph said Eliza.

   _____

2. Esteban asked Has anyone seen my pink eraser?

   _____

3. Mr. Perez said Please pass your papers to the front of the room.

   _____

4. I need to go to the library to study for my test said Manuela.

   _____

5. I think the test will be hard Octal said to Mariana.

   _____

6. Isidro told Pico I have computer lab next period.

   _____

7. I have to work very hard in my science class replied Lupe.

   _____

8. Please pay attention! the teacher told her students.

   _____

ELD Standard
   Edit writing for grammatical structures and the mechanics of writing.
ELA Standard
   Use quotation marks around the exact words of a speaker.

Name _____   Date _____

ⓐ Declarative, Interrogative, and Imperative Sentences

✔ Declarative sentences state facts. Interrogative sentences ask questions and end with a question mark. Imperative sentences give commands.

■ Label each sentence as either *declarative*, *interrogative* or *imperative*. Then add the correct punctuation at the end of the sentence, as in the example.

Example:

My doctor moved back to Guatemala last year **.**

type of sentence: _____ declarative _____

1. You must all study very hard for the test tomorrow __

   type of sentence: _____

2. What did you bring for lunch today __

   type of sentence: _____

3. Stop tapping your foot so loudly on the floor __

   type of sentence: _____

4. Who can tell me the answer to question number 2 __

   type of sentence: _____

■ Write three original sentences on the lines below: one declarative, one interrogative, and one imperative.

Declarative:

1. _____

Interrogative:

2. _____

Imperative:

3. _____

ELD Standard
    Edit writing for basic conventions.
ELA Standard
    Identify types and structure of sentences.

5

Name _____   Date _____

b Alphabetical Order

━ ━ ━ ━ ━ ━ ━ ━ ━ ━ ━ ━ ━ ━ ━ ━ ━ ━ ━ ━

✔ When you put words in alphabetical order, you need to look at the first letter of each word. If the words begin with the same letter, then you have to look at the next letter in each word.

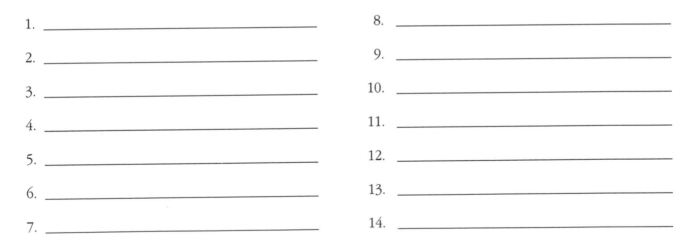

greeting	hello
morning	friendly
polite	uniform
help	please
afternoon	answer
attention	classroom
lunchroom	welcome

Example: p**a**y   p**l**ease   p**o**lite

━ ━ ━ ━ ━ ━ ━ ━ ━ ━ ━ ━ ━ ━ ━ ━ ━ ━ ━ ━

■ Alphabetize the words in the oval above by writing them on the numbered lines below.

1. _____   8. _____

2. _____   9. _____

3. _____   10. _____

4. _____   11. _____

5. _____   12. _____

6. _____   13. _____

7. _____   14. _____

ELD Standard
    Arrange words in alphabetical order.
ELA Standard
    Demonstrate alphabet principle.

Name _____   Date _____

◨ Verbs and Nouns

▬ ▬

✔ A noun is the name of a person, place, or thing. Verbs are the action words in a sentence.

▬ ▬

■ Read the words below and determine if they are nouns or verbs. Write the words in the appropriate columns.

Words	Verb	Noun
classroom		
jump		
cafeteria		
greet		
office		
athletic field		
auditorium		
eat		
computer lab		

■ Read the sentences below. Fill in the blanks with either a noun or a verb, as indicated by the prompt.

Example:

I _____study_____ with my partner, Luisa, in computer lab. (verb)

1. I like to _____ out on the athletic field at school. (verb)

2. I left my _____ on the table in science class. (noun)

3. How far did you _____ in P.E.? (verb)

4. I went to the mall because I needed to buy some _____. (noun)

5. I asked for a new _____ for my birthday. (noun)

6. Last night, I had to _____ for two whole hours! (verb)

7. Did you _____ at the meeting of the Science Club? (verb)

ELD Standard
  Use correct parts of speech.
ELA Standard
  Identify all parts of speech.

7

Name _____   Date _____

b Expository Writing

✔ Expository writing informs the reader about a topic. It can explain how to do something, or it can explain what happened.

■ Write five sentences describing how to turn on a computer and begin working on a project or program.

How to use a computer:

1. _____

2. _____

3. _____

4. _____

5. _____

■ Choose your favorite sport and write five sentences that tell about how to play it.

Name of sport: _____

1. _____

2. _____

3. _____

4. _____

5. _____

ELD Standard
Write expository compositions, that include a main idea and some details in simple sentences.
ELA Standard
Include the main idea and most significant details.

Name _____   Date _____

a The Verb *To Be*/Subject–Verb Agreement

▬ ▬ ▬ ▬ ▬ ▬ ▬ ▬ ▬ ▬ ▬ ▬ ▬ ▬ ▬ ▬ ▬ ▬ ▬

✔ Deciding which present-tense form of the verb *to be* is correct in a sentence depends on whether the subject of the sentence is singular or plural.

   Example: The student **is** working on the computer. (**subject**: student = singular)

   The students **are** working on the computer. (**subject**: students = plural)

▬ ▬ ▬ ▬ ▬ ▬ ▬ ▬ ▬ ▬ ▬ ▬ ▬ ▬ ▬ ▬ ▬ ▬ ▬

■ Read the passage below. Wherever there is a blank space, determine whether the subject is singular or plural, then fill in the correct form of the verb *to be* in the space.

Thursday _____ my favorite day because I like to buy my lunch in the school cafeteria. There _____

always several things that I really like. If there _____ chicken, I always buy it. If there _____

hamburgers and spaghetti, I usually get the spaghetti. There _____ a cafeteria worker who makes

delicious cakes and pies. Every Thursday there _____ cookies and brownies, as well. There _____

lots of reasons why I like to buy lunch in the cafeteria, but I think the main one _____ because I love

the desserts!

▬ ▬ ▬ ▬ ▬ ▬ ▬ ▬ ▬ ▬ ▬ ▬ ▬ ▬ ▬ ▬ ▬ ▬ ▬

■ Write the correct form of the verb *to be* (*is* or *are*) next to each word.

the teachers   _____   my neighbor   _____

the computer   _____   all the students   _____

the schools   _____   my science textbook   _____

the utensils   _____   the cafeteria   _____

all the lunches   _____   your lunchbox   _____

spaghetti   _____   brownies   _____

Saturdays   _____   a friend   _____

ELD Standard
   Use correct parts of speech, including correct subject–verb agreement.
ELA Standard
   Identify all parts of speech.

Name _____   Date _____

b Capitalization

✔ Capital letters are always used when referring to specific people, places or the names of the days of the week.

■ Read the words in the left-hand column. In the next column, rewrite the words that should be written with a capital letter because they are either the name of a person, place, or day of the week. In the last column, write *person*, *place* or *day of week*, depending upon which one describes the word.

Words	Proper Nouns	Description
government		
california		
maria montero		
lab		
thursday		
san diego		
weekday		
wednesday		
science		
cesar chavez		
athletic field		
peck memorial field		
boston		
friday		
utensils		

ELD Standard
Produce independent writing with consistent use of capitalization, punctuation, and correct spelling.
ELA Standard
Use correct capitalization.

Name _____   Date _____

a Subjects and Predicates

✔ The subject of a sentence tells who or what the sentence is about. The predicate of a sentence tells what happened. The simple subject is the main word or group of words in the complete subject.

■ Read each sentence and pay attention to the underlined words. On the line that follows each sentence, write the word *subject* or *predicate*, depending upon which one is underlined.

1. The boy <u>spins</u> the basketball on his fingers. _____

2. <u>I</u> leave school every day at 3:10. _____

3. <u>Everyone</u> has a locker in the hallway of our school. _____

4. Esmeralda <u>keeps</u> ten books in her locker. _____

5. Rogelio <u>scored</u> two goals in the game. _____

6. <u>The girls</u> talked during lunch break. _____

7. <u>Five of us</u> ride the bus to and from school. _____

The Subject	**The Predicate**
=	=
tells who or what the sentence is about	tells what happens

■ Complete the following sentences by filling in the missing words.

The _____ of a sentence tells who or _____ the

sentence is about. The predicate tells _____ _____.

The simple _____ is the main _____ or group of

words in the complete _____.

ELD Standard
Use correct parts of speech.
ELA Standard
Identify all parts of speech.

11

Name _____   Date _____

b Punctuation

✔ When you write times, use a colon to separate the hour and the minutes.

■ Write the following times using numbers and a colon.

Example: **three fifteen** _____3:15_____

four forty-five _____   one ten _____

two thirty _____   six twenty-five _____

nine fifty-five _____   ten forty _____

five minutes after seven _____   thirty minutes after eight _____

twenty minutes before five _____   eleven twenty-five _____

three fifty _____   two fifteen _____

■ Write the time that you might do the following activities. Write *A.M.* if this activity takes place in the morning, and *P.M.* if it takes place in the afternoon or evening.

Example: **wake up in the morning:** ____6:30 A.M.____

1. start your first class of the day at school: _____

2. catch the bus to get to school: _____

3. eat lunch: _____

4. attend a meeting of the computer club: _____

5. eat dinner: _____

6. do your homework: _____

7. ride the bus home from school: _____

8. go to bed at night: _____

9. watch your favorite television program: _____

10. last class of the day at school: _____

ELD Standard
Edit writing for basic conventions.
ELA Standard
Use a colon to separate hours and minutes.

Name _____   Date _____

a Possessive Nouns

▬ ▬ ▬ ▬ ▬ ▬ ▬ ▬ ▬ ▬ ▬ ▬ ▬ ▬ ▬ ▬ ▬ ▬ ▬

✔ The way to show that something belongs to someone (or something) is to use an apostrophe and the letter *s*. This is called the possessive case and it applies to nouns.

▬ ▬ ▬ ▬ ▬ ▬ ▬ ▬ ▬ ▬ ▬ ▬ ▬ ▬ ▬ ▬ ▬ ▬ ▬

▪ Form the possessive of these nouns, following the example.

Example:

the backpack that belongs to Concepcion: _____ Concepcion's backpack _____

the medical bag of Dr. Adam   _____

the purse of Mrs. Calderon   _____

the tape recorder of Ramon   _____

the monitor of the computer   _____

the eraser on the pencil   _____

tapes for the VCR   _____

the job of the librarian   _____

the globe in the classroom   _____

the locker that Patricia uses   _____

the report cards of Salvador   _____

▬ ▬ ▬ ▬ ▬ ▬ ▬ ▬ ▬ ▬ ▬ ▬ ▬ ▬ ▬ ▬ ▬ ▬ ▬

▪ Write five more examples of possessive nouns on the lines below. Circle the apostrophe and *s* in each one.

1. _____

2. _____

3. _____

4. _____

5. _____

ELD Standard
    Read and use contractions.
ELA Standard
    Use apostrophes in the possessive case of nouns.

Name _____   Date _____

b Plural Nouns

▬ ▬

✔ To change a singular noun into a plural noun, you usually add *s* or *es* to the word. When the noun ends with an *s*, you add *es*. When the noun ends with *y*, the *y* is dropped and *ies* is added. When a noun ends in *f*, change the *f* to a *v* and add *es*.

▬ ▬

■ Select the correct spelling of the plural form of the nouns below. Mark an **x** next to the word with the correct plural form.

1. leaf

   ❏ leafes   ❏ leafs   ❏ leaves

2. pony

   ❏ ponies   ❏ ponys   ❏ ponyies

3. class

   ❏ class's   ❏ classies   ❏ classes

4. library

   ❏ libraries   ❏ librarys   ❏ librares

5. language

   ❏ languagies   ❏ languages   ❏ language's

6. globe

   ❏ globs   ❏ globe's   ❏ globes

7. compass

   ❏ compasses   ❏ compass'   ❏ compass'ss

▬ ▬

■ Write the plural of the following words.

necklace _____

monitor _____

party _____

candy _____

meal _____

cafeteria _____

sharpener _____

bus _____

▬ ▬

■ Is this plural correct?

country = countries   Yes ❏   No ❏

stage = stage's   Yes ❏   No ❏

canvass = canvasses   Yes ❏   No ❏

diary = diarys   Yes ❏   No ❏

ELD Standard
Identify and correctly use regular and irregular plurals.
ELA Standard
Identify and correctly use regular and irregular plurals.

Name _____   Date _____

ᵃ Asking Questions

▬ ▬ ▬ ▬ ▬ ▬ ▬ ▬ ▬ ▬ ▬ ▬ ▬ ▬ ▬ ▬ ▬ ▬ ▬ ▬

Who?	What?	Where?	When?	Why?	Which?

✔ Questions are asked using the words *who, what, where, when, why,* and *which.*

▬ ▬ ▬ ▬ ▬ ▬ ▬ ▬ ▬ ▬ ▬ ▬ ▬ ▬ ▬ ▬ ▬ ▬ ▬ ▬

■ Write questions that will help you find out information, as in the following example. Be sure to end each question with a question mark. Circle the question word in each sentence.

Example:

to find out the location of the science class: _____ (Where) is the science class? _____

1. to find out which person can help you in the office:

   _____

2. to find out the reason for the ringing of the bell:

   _____

3. to find out the location of the school athletic field:

   _____

4. to ask the best route to get to school:

   _____

5. to find out the name of an unknown item:

   _____

6. to ask about the time:

   _____

7. to find out which teacher is in charge in the computer lab:

   _____

8. to find out the time that the bus arrives:

   _____

ELD Standard
   Participate in social conversations with peers and adults on familiar topics by asking and answering questions and soliciting information.
ELA Standard
   Identify types and structure of sentences.

15

Name _____   Date _____

b Capitalization and Punctuation

▪ Read the following paragraph. It describes books made in ancient China. The paragraph is missing punctuation and capital letters. Rewrite the paragraph on the lines below, adding the needed punctuation and correct capital letters.

the oldest books from china were known as slat books___ a cord held pieces of bamboo or strips of wood together___ these books folded up like accordions or were sometimes rolled___ this was how slat books were stored___ slat books were used for mathematics and for different kinds of record-keeping___ these books haven't been made in china for 1___600 years___ have you ever seen a sample of a slat book___

_____

_____

_____

_____

_____

_____

▪ Use the title page below to answer the following questions.

1. What is the title of the book?

   _____

2. Who is the publisher?

   _____

3. Who is the author?

   _____

4. When was the book published?

   _____

Puerto Rican Cookbook
La cocina boricua

By Efrain Santa

Printed in 2003

Santillana USA Publishing Company
Miami, Florida

ELD Standard
   Point out text features, such as the title, table of contents, and chapter headings.
ELA Standard
   Use correct capitalization and punctuation.

Name _____   Date _____

ⓐ Compound Words

━ ━ ━ ━ ━ ━ ━ ━ ━ ━ ━ ━ ━ ━ ━ ━ ━ ━ ━

✔ Compound words are made up of two separate words that are put together.

  Example: basket + ball = basketball

━ ━ ━ ━ ━ ━ ━ ━ ━ ━ ━ ━ ━ ━ ━ ━ ━ ━ ━

■ Combine one word from Column A with a word from Column B to form a new compound word. Then look up the meaning of five of the words in the dictionary and write the definitions in the box below.

A	B		
score	craft	1.	_____
camp	fly	2.	_____
bees	wax	3.	_____
news	ground	4.	_____
foot	vine	5.	_____
air	board	6.	_____
grape	paper	7.	_____
stop	boy	8.	_____
butter	stool	9.	_____
school	watch	10.	_____

Definitions:

1. _____

2. _____

3. _____

4. _____

5. _____

ELD Standard
  Use a standard dictionary to determine the meaning of unknown words.
ELA Standard
  Spell correctly compound words.

Name _____   Date _____

b Parts of Speech

━ ━

✔ Nouns are the names of people, places or things. Verbs are the action words in a sentence.

━ ━

■ Read each sentence. Decide what part of speech the underlined word is, and mark the correct answer option next to it.

Example:

I have played on a basketball <u>team</u> for three years.   _____ verb   __✔__ noun

1. Our school has a new football <u>coach</u>.   _____ verb   _____ noun

2. Who <u>taught</u> you to throw a football?   _____ verb   _____ noun

3. Did you <u>buy</u> a new uniform?   _____ verb   _____ noun

4. I'll meet you on the <u>playground</u>!   _____ verb   _____ noun

5. I found a <u>helmet</u> on the athletic field.   _____ verb   _____ noun

6. We'll play the next game in the <u>gym</u>.   _____ verb   _____ noun

7. That girl can really <u>kick</u> the ball!   _____ verb   _____ noun

8. We have a new <u>teammate</u>.   _____ verb   _____ noun

9. Pablo <u>runs</u> very fast!   _____ verb   _____ noun

10. What is your favorite <u>sport</u>?   _____ verb   _____ noun

11. I <u>joined</u> the team last week.   _____ verb   _____ noun

12. Can you <u>see</u> where the ball went?   _____ verb   _____ noun

18   **ELD Standard**
      Use correct parts of speech.
    ELA Standard
      Identify all parts of speech.

Name _____   Date _____

a Capitalization

✔ The following always have a capital letter:
- people's names
- the days of the week
- the months of the year
- specific places
- holidays

- Write each word below in the correct box, according to its category. Be sure to capitalize the words when you write them in the boxes.

wednesday	february	november	easter	angel
omar	christmas	friday	tuesday	thanksgiving
lilia	chicago	july	spain	los angeles
sunday	miami	beatriz	january	halloween

People's names:

_____ _____ _____ _____

Days of the week:

_____ _____ _____ _____

Months of the year:

_____ _____ _____ _____

Places:

_____ _____ _____ _____

Holidays:

_____ _____ _____ _____

ELD Standard
    Edit writing for punctuation, capitalization and spelling.
ELA Standard
    Use correct capitalization.

19

Name _____   Date _____

b Possessive Nouns

✔ The way to show that something belongs to someone (or something) is to use an apostrophe and the letter *s*. This is called the possessive case and it applies to nouns.

■ Underline the noun in each sentence that should be possessive. Then write it correctly after the sentence. The first one is already done.

1. The <u>Pilgrims</u> ship was called the Mayflower.   _____Pilgrims'_____

2. Mr. Thompson class is in the science lab.   _____

3. My sister attitude got her into trouble.   _____

4. Carlos grades were very encouraging.   _____

5. The team uniforms are red and yellow.   _____

6. We were surprised by Andrea reaction.   _____

7. Esperanza car is in the garage.   _____

8. The family enjoyed the children songs.   _____

9. My brothers names are Jorge and Eduardo.   _____

10. Have you seen the cat collar?   _____

■ Name some of the words that must be capitalized. The first is already done.

1. Names of cities. _____

2. _____

3. _____

4. _____

5. _____

ELD Standard
Read and use contractions.
ELA Standard
Use apostrophes in the possessive case of nouns.

Name _____   Date _____

a The Verb *To Be*

✔ Verbs are words that show an action that the subject performs. Verbs can also link the subject of the sentence to a complement (that which helps to describe or identify the subject.)

Example: **The cat jumps up and down.** (jumps = action verb) **The cat is happy.** (is = linking verb)

✔ The most common linking verb is the verb *to be*. This verb is written differently depending on whether the activity was in the past or is in the present.

Present Tense	Past Tense
(I) **am**	(I) **was**
(you) **are**	(you) **were**
(he, she, it) **is**	(he, she, it) **was**
(we) **are**	(we) **were**
(you, singular) **are**	(you, plural) **were**
(they) **are**	(they) **were**

■ Fill in the correct form of the past tense of the verb *to be* in the sentences below.

1. The teacher _____ explaining the science lesson to the students.

2. I _____ using headphones in the computer lab.

3. It _____ a fun computer game!

4. We _____ looking through microscopes in science class.

5. They _____ at their graduation last Tuesday night.

6. She _____ wearing a bright blue cap and gown.

7. _____ you happy when you got your diploma?

■ Write three more sentences using the past tense of the verb *to be*.

1. _____

2. _____

3. _____

ELD Standard
Use correct parts of speech, including correct subject-verb agreement.
ELA Standard
Identify and use subject and verb correctly.

21

Name _____   Date _____

b Verbs and Nouns

▬ ▬ ▬ ▬ ▬ ▬ ▬ ▬ ▬ ▬ ▬ ▬ ▬ ▬ ▬ ▬ ▬ ▬

✔ Verbs are action words. Nouns are words that name a person, place, thing, or idea.

▬ ▬ ▬ ▬ ▬ ▬ ▬ ▬ ▬ ▬ ▬ ▬ ▬ ▬ ▬ ▬ ▬

■ Read the list of words below and determine if each is a noun or a verb. Write the word in the appropriate column of the chart.

Words	Verb	Noun
draws		
worked		
typing		
education		
elementary school		
laboratory		
microscope		
slid		
student		
teach		
test tube		
woodshop		

■ Look around the classroom and find ten nouns. Write them on the lines below.

Nouns:

1. _____   6. _____

2. _____   7. _____

3. _____   8. _____

4. _____   9. _____

5. _____   10. _____

ELD Standard
   Understand and follow simple written directions for classroom-related activities.
ELA Standard
   Identify parts of speech.

■ Write four verbs that tell what you and your classmates are doing.

Verbs:

1. _____   3. _____

2. _____   4. _____

Name _____   Date _____

ⓐ Present Progressive

▬▬ ▬ ▬▬ ▬▬ ▬▬ ▬ ▬▬ ▬ ▬▬ ▬▬ ▬ ▬▬ ▬▬ ▬ ▬▬ ▬ ▬▬ ▬

✔ The tense of a verb tells when the action happens. There are different ways to show an "action" happening in the present. One way is to use the simple present tense. Another is to use the present progressive, which is formed by using a "helping" verb and then adding *ing* to the end of the main verb.

Examples: helps — *is* help*ing*

make — *are* mak*ing*

✔ Rules for forming the present progressive tense by adding *ing* to the main verb:

- **Rule #1:** For most verbs, add *ing*:

   Present tense: fall

   Present progressive tense: is/are falling

- **Rule #2:** For verbs that end in silent *e*, drop the *e*, and add *ing*

   Present tense: close

   Present progressive tense: is/are closing

- **Rule #3:** For verbs ending in a vowel and consonant, double the consonant, and add *ing*:

   Present tense: tap

   Present progressive tense: is/are tapping

▬▬ ▬ ▬▬ ▬▬ ▬▬ ▬ ▬▬ ▬ ▬▬ ▬▬ ▬ ▬▬ ▬▬ ▬ ▬▬ ▬ ▬▬ ▬

- Use each word below to write a sentence, using the present progressive tense. Circle each verb.

   Example:

   (start)   She is (starting) her report on Missionary Schools. _____

   1. (study)   _____

   2. (build)   _____

   3. (teach)   _____

   4. (listen) _____

   5. (ride)   _____

ELD Standard
   Read and use inflectional forms.
ELA Standard
   Identify and correctly use parts of speech.

Name _____   Date _____

b Regular and Irregular Verbs in the Past Tense

▬ ▬ ▬ ▬ ▬ ▬ ▬ ▬ ▬ ▬ ▬ ▬ ▬ ▬ ▬ ▬ ▬ ▬ ▬ ▬

✔ The past tense of a regular verb is formed by adding *ed*: **start = started**
✔ All other verbs are irregular and have special endings.

▬ ▬ ▬ ▬ ▬ ▬ ▬ ▬ ▬ ▬ ▬ ▬ ▬ ▬ ▬ ▬ ▬ ▬ ▬ ▬

■ Read the verbs in the banner below. Decide whether they are regular or irregular verbs, then write each one in the appropriate column.

gave	believed	got	wanted	kept
felt	changed	protected	enjoyed	were

Regular Verbs	**Irregular Verbs**
_____	_____
_____	_____
_____	_____
_____	_____
_____	_____

▬ ▬ ▬ ▬ ▬ ▬ ▬ ▬ ▬ ▬ ▬ ▬ ▬ ▬ ▬ ▬ ▬ ▬ ▬ ▬

■ Write the past tense of the following verbs.

1. clear _____   5. make _____

2. refuse _____   6. write _____

3. build _____   7. pull _____

4. like _____   8. know _____

ELD Standard
    Read and use inflectional forms.
ELA Standard
    Identify and use regular and irregular verbs.

25

Name   Date

◻ Demonstrative Pronouns

✔ The words *this* and *these* are demonstrative pronouns. Demonstrative pronouns point out a person or object referred to previously in a sentence.

■ Look at each picture. Complete each sentence by filling in the blank with the proper demonstrative pronoun *this* or *these*.

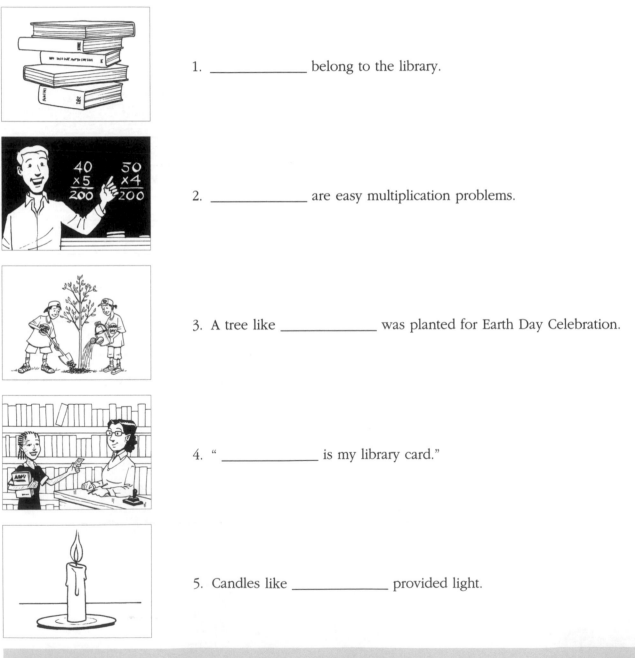

1. _____ belong to the library.

2. _____ are easy multiplication problems.

3. A tree like _____ was planted for Earth Day Celebration.

4. " _____ is my library card."

5. Candles like _____ provided light.

ELD Standard
   Identify and use parts of speech.
ELA Standard
   Make clear references between pronouns and antecedents.

■ Draw a picture in each figure, and write a sentence to go with it. Make sure each sentence includes the demonstrative pronoun *this* or *these*.

Name _____   Date _____

b Regular Verbs in the Past Tense/Demonstrating Comprehension

Education in Early America

Girls and boys received very different types of education in early America. A girl's household responsibilities were considered far more important than her academic instruction. Girls who were from wealthy families stayed at home where they received their education in such things as sewing, dancing, writing, and music. They also learned art, French, cooking, weaving, and nursing. They were frequently taught by a governess (often from England) and were taught how to "carry themselves" and how to act in polite company. A boy's education included reading, writing, simple math, poems, and prayers—what amounted to more advanced academics.

■ Read the selection, "Education in Early America." Underline each regular past tense verb. Then answer the following questions about the reading selection, using complete sentences.

1. What was considered more important in a girl's life than her education?

   _____

2. Who often taught girls in their homes?

   _____

3. What subjects did boys study in early America?

   _____

4. Where did many governesses come from?

   _____

5. What are some of the subjects that were taught to girls?

   _____

ELD Standard
   Read and use inflectional forms.
ELA Standard
   Demonstrate comprehension by identifying answers in the text.

Name _____   Date _____

a Present Progressive

▬ ▬ ▬ ▬ ▬ ▬ ▬ ▬ ▬ ▬ ▬ ▬ ▬ ▬ ▬ ▬

■ Rewrite each sentence, changing the verb in the present tense to the present progressive tense. Underline the verbs in the present progressive tense, as well as the "helping verbs."

Example:

Robert and Miguel **read** the primer with their teacher.

Robert and Miguel <u>are reading</u> the primer with their teacher. _____

1. The students **sit** on long benches in the classroom.

   _____

2. The boys **listen** attentively as the teacher explains the lesson.

   _____

3. The teacher **wears** a white apron over her dress.

   _____

4. She **writes** vocabulary words on the chalkboard.

   _____

5. The students' papers **sit** on the teacher's desk.

   _____

▬ ▬ ▬ ▬ ▬ ▬ ▬ ▬ ▬ ▬ ▬ ▬ ▬ ▬ ▬ ▬

■ Write the present progressive form of each of the following verbs.

Example:

   sing   _____ singing _____

1. copy   _____   6. teach   _____

2. stop   _____   7. wash   _____

3. eat   _____   8. try   _____

4. change   _____   9. continue _____

5. give   _____   10. leave   _____

ELD Standard
     Use correct parts of speech, including correct subject-verb agreement.
ELA Standard
     Demonstrate appropriate English usage.

29

Name   Date
_____   _____

ⓑ Identifying Main Idea and Supporting Details

▬▬ ▬▬ ▬▬ ▬▬ ▬▬ ▬▬ ▬▬ ▬▬ ▬▬ ▬▬ ▬▬ ▬▬ ▬▬ ▬▬ ▬▬ ▬▬

■ Read the passage below. Then answer the questions about the main idea and supporting details of each paragraph.

Tenement Schools

Tenement, or urban, schools are often used to illustrate all the things wrong with public education. While it is true that these schools may have overcrowding, crime, poverty, and other challenges not often faced in suburban schools, urban schools have also provided the benefits of diversity to the society at large.

Historically, the United States has been a nation where its large cities have played a major role in shaping the nation's culture and values. Beginning with the large influx of immigrants to the cities in the early 1900s, the arrival of many people to the urban areas during the Industrial Revolution and throughout the 20th Century forever changed our nation. For the first time, rich and poor individuals, people who spoke different languages, lived in the same neighborhoods and their children attended the same schools: primarily urban schools.

In the early 1960s, urban schools became the "testing grounds" for challenging segregation. Urban schools allowed black and white children to attend the same schools. This made it clear to the society at large that the United States would not tolerate prejudice and would strive to be a model of freedom. Later, similar movements against discrimination based on language and physical handicaps played out in urban schools. Urban schools have, indeed, provided many benefits to American society.

▬▬ ▬▬ ▬▬ ▬▬ ▬▬ ▬▬ ▬▬ ▬▬ ▬▬ ▬▬ ▬▬ ▬▬ ▬▬ ▬▬ ▬▬ ▬▬

1a. What is the main idea in the first paragraph?

_____

_____

1b. What are two supporting details?

_____

_____

2a. What is the main idea in the second paragraph?

_____

_____

ELD Standard
   Identify and explain the main ideas and critical details of informational materials, literary texts and texts in content areas.
ELA Standard
   Distinguish the main idea and supporting details in expository text.

2b. What are two supporting details?

_____

_____

3a. What is the main idea in the third paragraph?

_____

_____

3b. What are two supporting details?

_____

_____

Name _____   Date _____

ⓐ Regular Past Tense Verbs

━ ━ ━ ━ ━ ━ ━ ━ ━ ━ ━ ━ ━ ━ ━ ━ ━ ━ ━ ━

✔ Verbs are action words that describe what people do. The verb can tell the reader when the action took place by the way it is written. One common way to make a present tense verb into a past tense verb is to add the suffix *ed* to the end.

✔ Most verbs follow this rule with the following considerations:

If the verb ends with the letter *e*:	Change the *e* to *ed*: guide = guided
If the verb's last two letters are a vowel and a consonant:	Double the consonant and add *ed*: tap = tapped
If the verb ends in a consonant and *y*	Drop the *y* and add *ied*: study = studied
If the verb ends in a vowel and *y*	Add *ed*: play = played

■ Select the correct form of the following regular verbs in the past tense. Put a ✔ next to the word where the past tense is spelled correctly. Then select five of the verbs and use them in complete sentences using the past tense. Circle the verb in each sentence.

1. cover

   ❑ coverred   ❑ coverd   ❑ covered

2. want

   ❑ wanted   ❑ wanteed   ❑ wantted

3. learn

   ❑ learnd   ❑ learnned   ❑ learned

4. copy

   ❑ copyed   ❑ copied   ❑ copyyied

5. drop

   ❑ dropped   ❑ droped   ❑ dropied

6. type

   ❑ typped   ❑ typd   ❑ typed

7. sew

   ❑ sewed   ❑ sewwied   ❑ sewwed

8. repair

   ❑ repairyed   ❑ repaired   ❑ repairrd

━ ━ ━ ━ ━ ━ ━ ━ ━ ━ ━ ━ ━ ━ ━ ━ ━ ━ ━ ━

Sentences:

1. _____

2. _____

3. _____

4. _____

5. _____

ELD Standard
  Edit writing for basic conventions.
ELA Standard
  Identify and use regular past tense verbs.

Name   Date

ⓑ Asking and Answering Questions

▬ ▬ ▬ ▬ ▬ ▬ ▬ ▬ ▬ ▬ ▬ ▬ ▬ ▬ ▬ ▬ ▬ ▬

✔ There are three types of sentences: declarative, interrogative, and exclamatory. An interrogative sentence asks a question and ends with a question mark. Many interrogative sentences, or questions, start with a question word (*who, what, where, why,* or *when*), and all of them end with a question mark.

Who	What	When	Where	Why
person	thing, idea	time	place	reason

■ Read each sentence. Then fill in the chart with the correct information by answering the questions *Who?, What?, When?, Where?,* or *Why?* Read each box carefully before answering the question.

1. In the late 19th Century women in large cities worked in factories sewing clothing.

Who?	What?	When?	Where?

2. Students in vocational schools studied typing so they could get a good job.

Who?	What?	Why?	Where?

3. Men learned welding so they could find work in the large factories.

Who?	What?	Why?	Where?

4. People studied architectural drawing in the 1930s, to build the skyscrapers in the cities.

Who?	What?	When?	Why?

ELD Standard
    Generate and respond to questions related to text.
ELA Standard
    Identify types and structure of sentences.

Name _____   Date _____

a Irregular Verbs in the Past Tense

■ Study the chart below. Read each verb in the present tense. Then read the same verb as it is written in the past tense. Then read the sentences below. Each one is missing the verb. Select the correct form of the verb and write it on the blank line.

Present Tense	Past Tense
lead	lead
go	went
bring	brought
think	thought
become	became

Present Tense	Past Tense
read	read
sit	sat
get	got
have	had
know	knew

1. After attending vocational school, the man (verb: to become) _____ a welder.

2. She told me she (verb: to know) _____ how long it takes to become an architect.

3. Last year I (verb: to think) _____ I wanted to become a teacher.

4. Who (verb: to read) _____ the chapter for yesterday's homework?

5. Last night my best friend (verb: to bring) _____ me a copy of the book for my report.

6. I (verb: to think) _____ I would go to the bookstore.

7. All my classmates (verb: to know) _____ the answers to the questions on yesterday's math test.

8. Last August my family (verb: to go) _____ to Mexico City to visit relatives.

9. Five people (verb: to sit) _____ here and waited for the bus.

10. I (verb: to get) _____ an A in typing class.

■ Write three sentences using the irregular past tense of verbs in the chart above.

1. _____

2. _____

3. _____

ELD Standard
    Edit writing for basic conventions.
ELA Standard
    Identify and use irregular past tense verbs.

Name _____   Date _____

b Proofreading and Editing

Example:

Before proofreading:

white childrena and black Childen attended schools that were spearate,but not equal,

After proofreading:

White children and black children attended schools that were separate, but not equal.

- Proofread and edit the following passage. Rewrite the passage in the space below.

When linda Brown was eight years old: she had to travel to the other side of Topeka, Kansas to attend primary school? Some of her Friends were, able to attend classes just a few blocks away at the nayborhood public school. Why was this! Linda Brown was black and HER friends were white. The topeka school system was. segregated on the basis of race. although this was legal at that time, Landi's parents went to court to try to change the law. They didn't feel that it was fair for peoplE to be discriminated against based on the color of their skin??

Their case went all the way to the U. States Supreme Court.(The lawyer who represented Linda Brown, Thurgood Marshall, wood eventually become the frist African-American Supreme Court justice?

_____

_____

_____

_____

_____

_____

_____

_____

_____

_____

_____

_____

ELD Standard
   Edit writing for basic conventions.
ELA Standard
   Identify types and structure of sentences.

■ Read each sentence below and decide whether it is a declarative, interrogative or exclamatory sentence. Then provide the correct punctuation at the end of each sentence.

1. Do you think it was fair for students to be forced to attend separate schools __

   Type of sentence: _____

2. How happy people were when Linda Brown won her case before the U.S. Supreme Court __

   Type of sentence: _____

3. Thurgood Marshall was the first black Supreme Court justice __

   Type of sentence: _____

4. How old was Linda Brown when her parents decided to challenge the law allowing school segregation __

   Type of sentence: _____

5. The case before the Supreme Court was called *Brown v. Board of Education* __

   Type of sentence: _____

6. Stop denying the children their right to attend their neighborhood schools __

   Type of sentence: _____

Name _____   Date _____

a Present Progressive Tense

━━━━━━━━━━━━━━━━━━━━━━━━━━━━━━━━━━

✔ The present progressive tense is formed with a "helping verb" and by adding *ing* to the end of the main verb. If the verb ends in *e*, the *e* is dropped before adding *ing*.

━━━━━━━━━━━━━━━━━━━━━━━━━━━━━━━━━━

> is attending
>
> is guarding
>
> is studying
>
> are carrying
>
> are protecting
>
> are marching
>
> are discussing
>
> is crossing

■ Complete each sentence using the correct verb form from the box.

1. The soldiers _____ rifles.

2. The young woman _____ the street.

3. The guards _____ alongside the students.

4. The boy _____ for his test.

5. Who _____ the students who are going to their classes?

6. The men in uniform _____ the student.

7. The young woman _____ a formerly segregated school.

8. The students _____ their school textbooks.

ELD Standard
    Read and use inflectional forms.
ELA Standard
    Identify and correctly use parts of speech.

37

Name _____   Date _____

b Demonstrating Comprehension

■ Read the following passage. Then answer the comprehension questions that follow, using complete sentences.

"Stand in the Schoolhouse Door"

Arkansas was not the only state experiencing a great social transformation during the period of the Civil Rights Movement. Alabama was also defying the Federal mandate to desegregate its public school system. Just like the Little Rock Nine, two black students from Alabama, Vivian Malone and James Hood, decided to challenge the policy of school segregation.

On June 11, 1963, the two students entered the campus of the University of Alabama to register. The then governor of the state, George C. Wallace, had made a campaign pledge to stand in the schoolhouse door to block integration of Alabama public schools. To prevent Wallace from obstructing the registration process, President John F. Kennedy decided to federalize the Alabama National Guard, and ordered its units to the university campus. Governor Wallace kept his promise as he stood in the doorway of the University of Alabama, trying to stop the two students from registering. As he was blocking the entrance, he read a proclamation accusing the Federal government of intrusion, and oppression of the rights and sovereignty of the state of Alabama. At the end, Wallace did not have any other choice but to step aside and allow the students to enter.

1. Where did Vivian Malone and James Hood live?

_____

2. What did they decide to challenge?

_____

3. What did the governor of Alabama do in reaction to the students' decision?

_____

4. When did the students enter the university campus?

_____

5. What were the students seeking?

_____

ELD Standard
   Respond to comprehension questions about text by using detailed sentences.
ELA Standard
   Compare and contrast information on the same topic after reading several passages.

6. How did the Federal government react to the Governor's defiance?

_____

7. How is this story similar to the story of the Little Rock Nine?

_____

■ Fill in the missing words, according to the information in the passage above.

1. Alabama was not the only state _____ a great social transformation.

2. The two students _____ the campus of the University of Alabama.

3. Governor George C. Wallace had made a campaign _____ to stand in the

_____ door.

4. Governor Wallace _____ his promise.

5. On June 11, 1963, Governor Wallace read a _____ accusing the Federal government of intrusion and oppression.

Name   Date
_____

a Present, Present Progressive, and Past Tense

✔ The tense of a verb shows when the action happens or happened. There are different ways to show an action happening in the present. One way is to use the **simple present tense**. Another is the **present progressive tense**, which is formed with a "helping verb" and by adding *ing* to the end of the main verb.

✔ The way to show that an action occurred in the past is to use the **simple past tense**. The simple past tense is formed by adding *ed* to the ending of most verbs. Sometimes, the verbs are irregular and their spelling changes in the past tense.

Examples: think ⟶ thought

ride ⟶ rode

■ Fill in the blank squares of the chart below, following the examples. Use the "helping verb" *is* with the present progressive tense.

Present Tense	Present Progressive Tense	Simple Past Tense
Example: hopes	**Example:** is hoping	**Example:** hoped
	is keeping	
goes		
		thought
rides		
	is studying	
		feared
marches		
attends		
		welcomed

ELD Standard
    Edit writing for basic conventions.
ELA Standard
    Demonstrate proper English usage.

Name   Date

b Descriptive Writing: Writing Sentences

- Write a paragraph using each of the following sentences as topic sentences or as the lead sentence in each paragraph.

1. African American students knew it was time for a change.

_____

_____

_____

_____

2. In Little Rock, nine African American students tested the new law.

_____

_____

_____

_____

3. The late 1950s was a time of change in the public schools in our southern cities.

_____

_____

_____

_____

4. Some white students and teachers were ready for desegregation.

_____

_____

_____

_____

ELD Standard
   Proceed through the writing process to write short paragraphs that contain supporting details about a given topic.
ELA Standard
   Convey clear and accurate perspectives on the subject.   41

Name _____   Date _____

a Identifying Facts and Opinions

▬ ▬ ▬ ▬ ▬ ▬ ▬ ▬ ▬ ▬ ▬ ▬ ▬ ▬ ▬ ▬ ▬ ▬ ▬

✔ An opinion is a thought or a belief. A fact is a true statement. Facts often have numbers and dates in them. Opinions usually have words that show emotion or judgment.

▬ ▬ ▬ ▬ ▬ ▬ ▬ ▬ ▬ ▬ ▬ ▬ ▬ ▬ ▬ ▬ ▬ ▬ ▬

■ Read the following article entitled "Bilingual Education and ESL." Then complete the exercises about identifying facts and opinions.

Bilingual Education and ESL

Before World War I, many schools offered instruction to students in English and the students' native languages. However, after World War I, anti-German sentiment led to a "backlash" against bilingual education and the result was that many people were discouraged from even speaking their native languages. It was not until the 1960s that this trend was reversed.

The Bilingual Education Act of 1968 was passed during a time when the Civil Rights Movement was in full force. It provided Federal funds to school districts so that they could begin to include native-language instruction in the curriculum. This was the first time Congress had endorsed funding for bilingual education. The Bilingual Education Act of 1968 made bilingual education programs mandatory.

The ultimate goal of any program is for students to become proficient in English. Recently, however, bilingual education has been at the center of controversy. While most people agree that the priorities in the education of immigrant students are fluency in English and proficiency in content areas, a heated political battle continues over how best to accomplish this. The question is how important it really is for students to be educated in their own language.

ELD Standard
  Distinguish explicit examples of facts, opinions, inference, and cause and effect in texts.
ELA Standard
  Distinguish between fact and opinion in an expository text.

■ Read each statement and then indicate whether it is a fact or an opinion by putting a check in the appropriate column of the chart. The first one is already done.

	FACT	OPINION
1. The Bilingual Education Act of 1968 made bilingual programs mandatory.	☑	❏
2. Bilingual education is the best way to teach children.	❏	❏
3. Anti-German sentiment led to a "backlash" against bilingual education.	❏	❏
4. Bilingual education is controversial.	❏	❏
5. It was unfortunate that people were discouraged from speaking their native languages.	❏	❏
6. The Bilingual Education Act of 1968 was the first time Congress had endorsed funding for bilingual education.	❏	❏
7. It is very important for students to be educated in their native language.	❏	❏

Name   Date
_____   _____

b Persuasive Writing

━━ ━━ ━ ━━ ━━ ━━ ━ ━ ━ ━━ ━━ ━━ ━━ ━ ━━ ━━ ━━ ━━ ━━ ━━ ━━

✔ It is important to express your opinions and beliefs. Writing your thoughts can persuade others to see your point of view.

✔ When you are writing a persuasive article remember to do the following:

   a) State your opinion.

   b) State the important facts of your argument.

   c) State reasons that support your opinion.

   d) Rephrase your original opinion in a summary.

━━ ━━ ━ ━━ ━━ ━━ ━ ━ ━ ━━ ━━ ━━ ━━ ━ ━━ ━━ ━━ ━━ ━━ ━━ ━━

▪ You have read an article entitled "Bilingual Education and ESL." Now write a paragraph or two giving your opinion on the subject of bilingual education. Be sure to follow the steps listed above. Think about the following questions as you write:

   ✔ *Do you believe that it is the best way to teach and learn?*

   ✔ *Do you have experience with bilingual education?*

   ✔ *Do you think it is better to just teach ESL?*

▪ Use complete sentences and express your opinions clearly.

_____
(Title)
_____
_____
_____
_____
_____
_____
_____
_____

ELD Standard
   Describe relationship between the text and one's personal experience.
ELA Standard
   Revise writing to improve organization and word choice after checking the logic of the ideas and the precision of the vocabulary.

Name _____   Date _____

a Identifying Main Ideas and Supporting Details

✔ The main idea of a passage tells what the passage is about.

Diversity brings educational benefits to all students and teachers, as well as to the wider community. It ensures that the school environment will be enriched by different life experiences and life perspectives. Students share their cultural traditions with their classmates. Everyone can be exposed to new languages. The attitudes and lessons learned by students in a diverse school environment parallel those needed for the adult life they will soon enter.

1. What is the main idea of this passage? _____

_____

_____

2. What are the supporting details? _____

_____

_____

_____

My name is Efrain. I use a wheelchair because my legs don't work quite right. The happiest day of my life was when I first got to my school and attended classes with all my friends. Before, I had to go to a special school, but now I can take part in all the activities and I never have to miss anything. Now I attend club meetings after school and play in the school band. People treat me just like everyone else! This is what I would tell anyone who asked me: it's great to go to school with all your friends. Just because you use a wheelchair doesn't change how you learn!

1. What is the main idea of this passage? _____

_____

_____

2. What are the supporting details? _____

_____

_____

_____

ELD Standard
   Identify and explain the main ideas and critical details of informational materials, literary texts, and texts in content areas.
ELA Standard
   Distinguish the main idea and supporting details in expository text.

Name   Date

b Writing an Essay

- Review the Writing Checklist at the end of this book. This will help you organize your essay. Then select one topic about education in the United States for your essay.

- Write your essay in the space provided below.

(Title)

ELD Standard
Proceed through the writing process to write short paragraphs that contain supporting details about a given topic.
ELA Standard
Identify topics, ask and evaluate questions, and develop ideas.

Name _____   Date _____

a Demonstrating Comprehension

- Read the passage. Then answer the questions that follow using complete sentences and the vocabulary words in the box at the bottom of the page.

P'an Ku
An Egyptian Myth

P'an Ku was the first living thing. He developed inside a gigantic cosmic egg, which held all the elements of the universe inside. P'an Ku grew by about 10 feet each day. As he grew, he separated the Earth and the Sky within the egg. At the same time he gradually separated the many opposites found in nature: wet and dry, light and dark, wet and dry male and female, etc. These were all originally totally contained together in the egg.

While P'an Ku grew, he also created the first people. After 18,000 years, the egg hatched and P'an Ku died from the exertion of creation. The sun and moon appeared from his eyes. Rain and dew came from his sweat, thunder from his voice, and all the natural features of the earth from his body.

1. What is the setting of this Egyptian myth?

   _____

2. Describe the main character in this myth.

   _____

3. Explain the plot.

   _____

   _____

   _____

Vocabulary Words

elements	cosmic	exertion	features
opposites	originally	creation	gigantic

ELD Standard
   Read a literary selection and explain the literary elements of plot, setting, and characters by using detailed sentences.
ELA Standard
   Identify events that advance the plot and determine how each event explains past or present action(s) or foreshadows future action(s).

Name _____   Date _____

b Story Mapping

■ Complete the story map with the most important information from the Egyptian myth, "P'an Ku."

Story Map

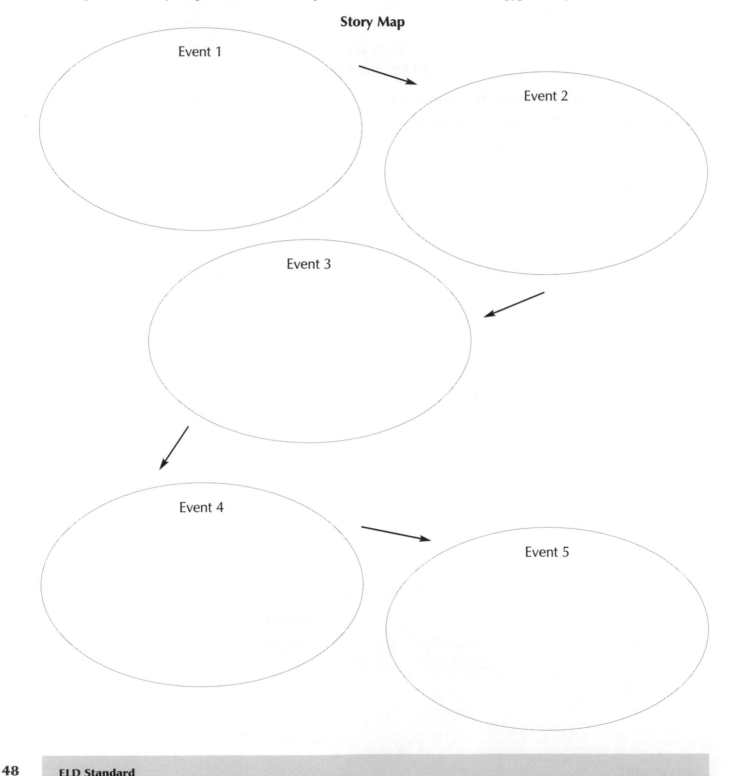

ELD Standard
    Organize and record information from selected literature and content areas by displaying it on pictures, lists, charts, and tables.
ELA Standard
    Identify events that advance plot and determine how each event explains past or present action(s) or foreshadows future action(s).

Name _____   Date _____

a Writing Superlative Sentences

━━ ━ ━━ ━ ━ ━ ━ ━━ ━ ━━ ━ ━ ━━ ━ ━ ━━ ━ ━ ━━ ━

✔ Adjectives are describing words that help you compare how things are the same or different. Adding *er* to the end of an adjective will help you compare two things. When you compare three or more things, you need to add *the* plus *est* to the end of the adjective. These sentences are called *superlative sentences.*

Example: She is a strong athlete. *(declarative sentence)*

She is **stronger** than he is. *(comparative sentence, comparing two things)*

She is **the strongest** athlete of the team. *(comparing more than two things)*

━━ ━ ━━ ━ ━ ━ ━ ━━ ━ ━━ ━ ━ ━━ ━ ━ ━━ ━ ━ ━━ ━

▪ Change each comparative sentence into a superlative sentence.

Example:

He is a faster runner than Mary.

He is **the fastest** runner of the group.

1. She is stronger than Lupe.

_____

2. He can throw a ball farther than Arjun can.

_____

3. Anil is taller than Kate.

_____

4. Grace can jump higher than her friend.

_____

5. Those are nice boxing gloves.

_____

6. That white horse is larger than all the others.

_____

ELD Standard
Edit and correct basic grammatical structures and usage of the conventions of writing.
ELA Standard
Demonstrate the mechanics of writing and appropriate English usage.

Name   Date

b Reading a Score Card

■ Look at the score card and answer the questions about it by marking the correct answers with an *x*.

Goals Scored:

	April	May	June	July	August
Pablo	1	3	1	3	2
Jose	0	2	0	1	0
Miguel	3	3	3	3	3
Ron	2	0	2	1	2
Frank	4	5	3	4	4

1. Who scored the most goals in May?

   ❑ Jose   ❑ Ron

   ❑ Pablo   ❑ Frank

2. Who scored the fewest goals in June?

   ❑ Ron   ❑ Jose

   ❑ Pablo   ❑ Miguel

3. How many goals did Miguel score in July?

   ❑ 2   ❑ 3

   ❑ 1   ❑ 0

4. Who scored the most goals in August?

   ❑ Jose   ❑ Pablo

   ❑ Frank   ❑ Ron

5. Who scored the fewest goals in April?

   ❑ Ron   ❑ Frank

   ❑ Jose   ❑ Miguel

6. Which two boys scored the same number of goals in May?

   ❑ Jose & Miguel

   ❑ Frank & Pablo

   ❑ Pablo & Miguel

ELD Standard
  Use common verbs, nouns, and high-frequency modifiers in simple sentences.
ELA Standard
  Locate information by using a variety of consumer, workplace, and public documents.

■ Write five sentences about the chart using comparatives or superlatives.

Example: Frank was the highest scoring player in May.

1. _____

2. _____

3. _____

4. _____

5. _____

Name   Date

a Subject Pronouns

- ✔ A subject pronoun takes the place of a subject noun. In using pronouns, it is important to be sure you are clear about the person and the number of people or objects you are referring to.
- ✔ When talking about yourself use *I* for singular, and *we* for more than one.

    Example: I am Sophia Petruncola. / We are the Petruncola sisters.

- ✔ When talking to somebody else use *you* for both, singular and plural.

    Example: You are my sister. / You are my brothers.

- ✔ When talking about other people use *you* for singular, and *they* for more than one.

    Example: You are the Giano brothers. / They are the Giano brothers.

- ✔ When talking about a thing use *it* for singular, and *they* for more than one.

    Example: It is a big building. / They are big buildings.

■ Rewrite the following sentences, replacing each noun with the correct pronoun.

1. The libraries were filled with books.

   _____

2. The actors gave a great performance.

   _____

3. The public appreciated the work of the water engineer.

   _____

4. The amphitheaters were made of stone.

   _____

5. The Emperor Justinian established the Byzantine empire.

   _____

6. The Roman Empire was powerful.

   _____

7. Rome was the center of a huge empire.

   _____

ELD Standard
    Edit and correct basic grammatical structures and usage of the conventions of writing.
ELA Standard
    Make clear references between pronouns and antecedents.

8. The Romans took control of Ephesus.

_____

9. Julius Caesar was a famous Roman emperor.

_____

10. Zenobia was a warrior queen, who led her people in a war against Rome.

_____

Name _____   Date _____

b Pronouns and Subject-Verb Agreement

■ Choose the correct verb to complete each sentence.

1. It _____ an extremely significant period in history. (was/were)

2. They _____ famous for their contributions to Western cultures. (is/are)

3. He _____ many territories during his reign. (conquer/conquered)

4. I _____ learning about the Roman and Greek empires. (am/is)

5. They _____ from around the world to see the famous buildings. (come/comes)

6. She _____ the wife of the emperor. (was/were)

7. It _____ a Roman amphitheater. (show/shows)

8. We _____ from different countries. (come/comes)

9. He _____ to read about ancient civilizations. (like/likes)

10. Where _____ you born? (was/were)

ELD Standard
  Use correct parts of speech, including correct verb–subject agreement.
ELA Standard
  Identify and use subject and verb correctly.

Name   Date

a Capitalization of Proper Nouns

✔ The names of people and places begin with capital letters.

■ Correct the following sentences by capitalizing all proper nouns. Write the sentences on the lines provided.

1. leonardo da vinci painted during the renaissance.

_____

2. He painted the *mona lisa*.

_____

3. leonardo was born in vinci, italy, outside of florence.

_____

4. michelangelo was another famous renaissance painter.

_____

5. botticelli painted the *birth of venus*.

_____

6. He painted three frescos in the sistine chapel.

_____

7. raphael was born in urbino, italy.

_____

8. cellini, a sculptor, created a statue of perseus.

_____

9. sir walter raleigh attended oxford and studied law in england.

_____

10. albrecht durer was born in nuremburg, germany, but lived many years in italy.

_____

ELD Standard
  Edit writing for basic conventions.
ELA Standard
  Use correct capitalization.

55

Name _____   Date _____

b Demonstrating Comprehension

■ Read the biography below about Leonardo da Vinci. Answer the comprehension questions that follow using complete sentences.

Leonardo da Vinci

Leonardo was born on April 15, 1452, in Vinci, Italy, just outside of Florence. He was raised by his father. In his father's Vinci home, Leonardo read many books and learned about painting traditions. At the age of 15, he became an apprentice in Florence and began to show his great talent. One of Leonardo's first paintings was of an angel and it turned out to be better than his teacher's.

In 1482, Leonardo went to Milan, where he spent 17 years. During these years he achieved even greater artistic, as well as scientific, achievement. It was here that he worked for the Duke of Milan painting and sculpting as "painter and engineer of the Duke." He was also asked to design buildings, weapons and machines. His drawings even included flying machines and studies of the human body! He was so busy drawing new things that he sometimes had trouble finishing one thing before moving on to the next!

In 1513, Leonardo was in Rome and did some projects for the Pope. His last position was in France, where his patron was King Francis I. Here he lived in the castle Cloux and was given the designation of "first painter, architect, and mechanic of the King." Leonardo da Vinci died on May 2, 1519 in Amboise on the Loire, France. He was a true genius, working in art, science and technology.

■ Answer the following questions using complete sentences.

1. Where was Leonardo da Vinci born?

_____

2. How old was Leonardo when he went to Florence as an apprentice?

_____

3. What was Leonardo's "title" when he worked for the Duke of Milan?

_____

4. What kinds of things did Leonardo design and draw when he was in Milan?

_____

5. When and where did he die?

_____

ELD Standard
Write simple sentences of brief responses to selected literature to show factual understanding of the text.
ELA Standard
Demonstrate comprehension by identifying answers in the text.

Name _____   Date _____

a Adjectives

✔ Adjectives describe the noun they precede in a sentence. Adjectives can describe the size, shape, color, quantity, look, feel, smell, sound, taste, etc., of a noun. Listed below are some adjectives that are used to describe nouns.

Size	Shape	Color	Quantity	Look	Feel	Sound	Taste	Emotion
big	oval	blue	first	beautiful	hard	loud	sweet	happy
little	square	green	second	fluffy	soft	quiet	salty	sad
huge	round	black	many	shiny	rough	noisy	sour	depressed
tiny	rectangular	ivory	some	gloomy	slimy	soft	hot	uplifting
large	triangular	white	none	dry	smooth	blaring	cold	serene

■ Create your own picture of a "perfect room," adding lots of color and design. Then write seven sentences describing the room. Be sure to use plenty of details in both your drawing and description. Use some of the words provided above in your sentences.

_____

_____

_____

_____

_____

_____

_____

ELD Standard
  Write simple compositions, such as descriptions and comparison and contrast, that have a main idea and some detail.
ELA Standard
  Place modifiers properly.

Name _____   Date _____

b Demonstrating Comprehension

━━━

■ Read the passage below and complete the Venn diagram.

People live differently all over the world. The way we live has inspired much of the art that surrounds us in our homes. Many homes in present-day countries that once made up Persia, reflect the culture that inspired their intricate and beautiful rugs. Some of the more traditional homes still maintain this style of ornate simplicity. Visiting a traditional country home in Iran, one might see a small two-room house, warmed by vibrant and welcoming fabrics. A sitting room might be covered by beautiful rugs and accented with pillows to sit and lean upon. The furniture would be low to the ground and you might also find a low dining table for meals. This is certainly different from our homes in the United States, where furniture is up off the floor. We tend to sit on couches and eat at tables and chairs that are elevated. We also tend to surround ourselves with more technological items, such as televisions and stereos. Although our homes are different from homes in the Middle East, we still have many things in common.

━━━

■ List four things that are different between your home and a Persian home, and four things that are the same. Then fill in the Venn diagram with the information.

Different:

1. _____   3. _____

2. _____   4. _____

Same:

1. _____   3. _____

2. _____   4. _____

PERSIAN HOMES   SAME   MY HOME

ELD Standard
    Organize and record information from selected literature and content areas by displaying it on pictures, lists, charts, and tables.
ELA Standard
    Identify and trace the development of an author's argument, point of view, or perspective in text.

Name _____   Date _____

a Demonstrating Comprehension: Summarizing

▪ Read the passage and then write five main points that summarize the paragraph. Make sure they are in the correct sequence.

The History of Chinese Writing

The first evidence of Chinese writing goes back to 1200 B.C. Bones with etched carvings in them from the Shang Dynasty demonstrated that even back then, the Chinese had a highly developed system of written communication. Other discoveries of Chinese writing were found in the Zhou dynasty, in existence during the Middle Ages. These samples of writing were bronze inscriptions, used for religious ceremonies. The writing of these bronze inscriptions was similar to that found on the bones. Modern Chinese writing emerged in the fifth century B.C. Writing samples were found etched on bamboo strips. The writings found on these strips, like the others, reflected religious and philosophical beliefs of the Chinese people. In 221 B.C., Emperor Qin standardized writing so that characters in all regions of the country were written in the same way. This gave birth to China's modern-day writing system.

Main points:

1. _____

2. _____

3. _____

4. _____

5. _____

ELD Standard
    Write simple sentences of brief responses to selected literature to show factual understanding of the text.
ELA Standard
    Include the main ideas and most significant details.

Name   Date

b Creating a Timeline

▬▬ ▬ ▬▬ ▬ ▬▬ ▬ ▬▬ ▬ ▬▬ ▬ ▬▬ ▬ ▬▬ ▬ ▬▬ ▬ ▬▬ ▬ ▬▬ ▬

✔ A timeline shows information in a particular way: facts are listed in the order in which they took place.

▬▬ ▬ ▬▬ ▬ ▬▬ ▬ ▬▬ ▬ ▬▬ ▬ ▬▬ ▬ ▬▬ ▬ ▬▬ ▬ ▬▬ ▬ ▬▬ ▬ ▬▬ ▬

■ Fill in facts from the article, "The History of Chinese Writing" in the boxes of the timeline below.

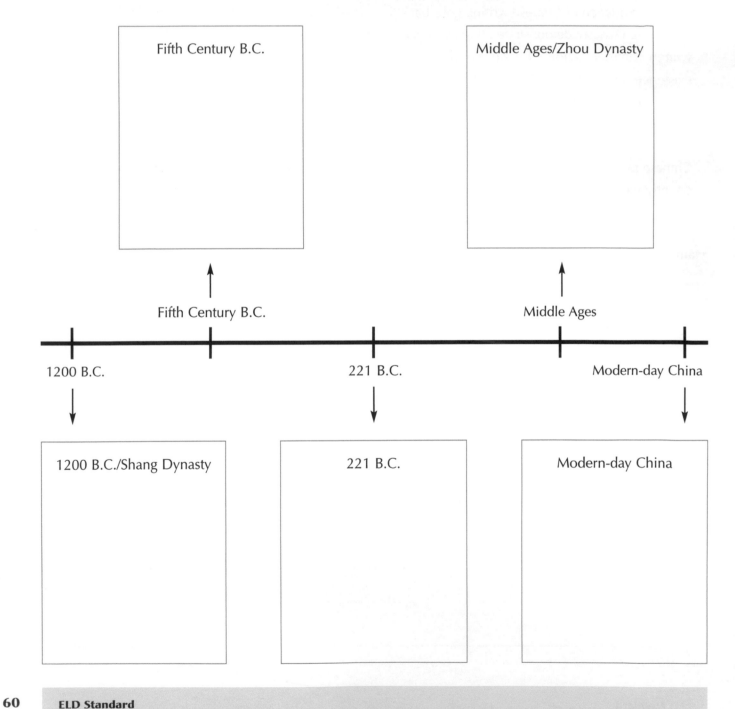

ELD Standard
   Organize and record information from selected literature and content areas by displaying it on pictures, lists, charts, and tables.
ELA Standard
   Convey clear and accurate perspectives on the subject.

Name   Date

a The Past Tense of Verbs Ending in *y* and Irregular Verbs

✔ Verbs are action words that describe what people do. The verb tells the reader when the action takes place (in the past, present, or future) usually by the way it is written. One common way to make a present tense verb into a past tense verb if the verb ends in a consonant and *y* is to drop the *y* and add *ied*: **study = studied.**

✔ Some verbs written in the past tense have very different forms from their present tense. They are called *irregular verbs*. The chart below shows some examples of common irregular verbs.

Present Tense	Past Tense
hear	heard
give	gave
hold	held
keep	kept
ride	rode
wear	wore
think	thought

■ Rewrite each of the following sentences in the past tense.

1. I <u>hear</u> a lot about how beautiful Persian rugs are.

_____

2. We <u>think</u> a lot about ancient Egypt.

_____

3. I <u>study</u> everything I could find about ancient Chinese writing.

_____

4. I <u>keep</u> all my books on the Renaissance in my room.

_____

5. I <u>rely</u> on my teacher for information on the Greeks and the Romans.

_____

ELD Standard
   Use common verbs, nouns, and high-frequency modifiers in writing simple sentences.
ELA Standard
   Identify and use regular and irregular past tense verbs.

61

6. I <u>take</u> many trips to the library to study about Leonardo da Vinci.

_____

7. I <u>will carry</u> the mask into the museum.

_____

■ Write a sentence with each of the following verbs, using the past tense: *give*, *hold*, and *ride*.

1. _____

2. _____

3. _____

Name _____   Date _____

b Common and Proper Nouns

✔ A common noun names **any** person, place, thing, or idea. A proper noun names a **specific** person, place, thing, or idea.

Example: The boy **dancer** demonstrates the dance of fertility. (common noun)

Hoksul demonstrates the dance of fertility. (proper noun)

■ Rewrite each sentence by inserting a proper noun to replace the common noun.

1. The **girl** prepared the dyes for the dancers.

   _____

2. A **dancer** stretches his muscles before the ceremony.

   _____

3. The **tribe** holds a feast to please the spirits.

   _____

4. The **town** prepares for visitors.

   _____

5. The **dance** sent shivers down my spine!

   _____

6. The **people** held different kinds of rituals and ceremonies.

   _____

7. The **man** wears a traditional mask representing a monkey.

   _____

ELD Standard
    Edit writing for basic conventions.
ELA Standard
    Use correct capitalization.

Name _____   Date _____

a Comparatives and Superlatives

▬▬ ▬▬ ▬▬ ▬▬ ▬▬ ▬▬ ▬▬ ▬▬ ▬▬ ▬▬ ▬▬ ▬▬ ▬▬ ▬▬

■ Use the passages below to write two comparative sentences and two superlative sentences about the Egyptian and Mayan pyramids.

Examples:

Comparative: The sky is bluer over the Mayan pyramid than the Egyptian pyramid. (Add *er* to the end of the adjective.)

Superlative: The Egyptian pyramid is the oldest pyramid in the world. (Add *the* + *est* to the adjective.)

Mayan Pyramids

The Mayan community of Chichen Itza flourished between 700 A.D. and 900 A.D. One of the structures found in this Mayan community is the Pyramid of Kukulkan. It is 79 feet high, and was built according to Mayan interests in astronomy and the calendar. Each of its sides had originally 91 steps, and if you add the platform at the top as a final step, there are 365 steps in total, one for each day of the year. Mayans used to build two types of pyramids. The first type was used for holding sacrificial rituals and the steps were used to climb. The second type was meant only to be touched since it was sacred, and its steps were too steep to climb. The Pyramid of Kukulkan was surrounded by different sacred buildings, including an observatory and the Ball Court.

Egyptian Pyramids

Egyptians began to build pyramids around 2780 B.C. One of the most famous pyramids in Egypt is the Great Pyramid at Giza. It is 450 feet high and it has smooth sides instead of steps. Early Egyptian pyramids were built by placing six mastabas, or bench-shaped mounds, in a stack to form a pyramid rising in steps. Egyptian pyramids did not stand alone, but were surrounded by a group of buildings that included temples, chapels, tombs, and massive walls. Pyramids were used as tombs for the mummified bodies of the kings.

Comparative:

1. _____

2. _____

Superlative:

1. _____

2. _____

ELD Standard
    Write simple sentences of brief responses to selected literature to show factual understanding of the text.
ELA Standard
    Identify types and structure of sentences.

Name _____   Date _____

b Action Verbs

■ Read the following facts about the Mayan civilization. Then make a list of the action verbs. Finally, use five of the verbs in new sentences.

MAYAN SOCIETY

1. The Mayans occupied the Yucatan Peninsula and were hunters and gatherers.
2. These people lived in small family bands.
3. The Mayan civilization originated in the Yucatan around 2600 B.C.
4. This civilization developed into highly structured kingdoms.
5. The Mayans used "slash-and-burn" techniques to clear the land.
6. The Mayans developed astronomy, calendars and hieroglyphic writing.
7. They planted maize, beans, squash and tobacco.
8. They lived in villages made up of households consisting of extended families.
9. The Mayan civilization produced temples and pyramids.
10. They worshipped hundreds of different gods.

Action verbs:

1. _____   6. _____
2. _____   7. _____
3. _____   8. _____
4. _____   9. _____
5. _____   10. _____

Sentences:

1. _____
2. _____
3. _____
4. _____
5. _____

ELD Standard
Use common verbs, nouns and high-frequency modifiers in writing simple sentences.
ELA Standard
Identify and use regular and irregular verbs.

Name _____   Date _____

ⓐ Asking and Answering Questions: Declarative and Interrogative Sentences

✔ A <u>declarative sentence</u> gives information and ends with a period. An <u>interrogative sentence</u> asks a question and ends with a question mark.

✔ To change a declarative sentence into an interrogative sentence, replace the subject or part of the predicate with the appropriate question word (*who, what, where, how,* or *when*), add helping verbs if necessary, and end with a question mark.

Declarative sentences:

The Chinampas grew crops.   The Aztecs lived **in present-day Mexico.**

Interrogative sentences:

Who grew crops?   **Where** did the Aztecs live?

■ Read the following passage and then write three questions from the facts stated in the passage. Then answer each question with a complete sentence.

> The Aztecs had one of the most advanced civilizations in North America. They achieved this distinction by conquering other advanced societies. The Aztec people were very religious, and this influenced many parts of their cultural life. They had pictographic writing, a mathematical system, and they were great astrologers. They learned from the Mayans how to calculate a solar year and they were able to create accurate solar calendars.

Example:

Question: _____ Who had one of the most advanced civilizations in North America _____?

Answer: _____ The Aztecs had one of the most advanced civilizations in North America. _____

1. _____?

_____

2. _____?

_____

3. _____?

_____

ELD Standard
   Generate and respond to questions related to text.
ELA Standard
   Identify types and structure of sentences.

Name _____   Date _____

b Irregular Verbs in the Past Tense

✔ Some verbs change the way they are written when they are written in past tense. They are called irregular verbs. The chart below shows you examples of many irregular verbs.

Present Tense	Past Tense
are	were
become	became
fall	fell
come	came

Present Tense	Past Tense
build	built
grow	grew
bring	brought
spin	spun

■ Rewrite the following statements about the Aztecs, replacing the present tense verbs in parentheses with the correct irregular form of the past tense.

1. The Aztecs (are) expert craftspeople.

   _____

2. Women (spin) cotton and maguey fibers into thread by twisting them onto a stick.

   _____

3. They (build) tall temples and huge sculptures.

   _____

4. On their fertile islands they (grow) squash, corn, vegetables and flowers.

   _____

5. Canoes (bring) the crops from nearby farms through the canals to markets in the capital, Tenochtitlan.

   _____

   _____

6. Decimated by the disease, the Aztec empire (fall).

   _____

7. They (become) the largest empire in Mesoamerica until they were conquered by Hernan Cortes.

   _____

ELD Standard
   Use common verbs, nouns and high-frequency modifiers in writing simple sentences.
ELA Standard
   Identify and use irregular past tense verbs.

67

Name _____   Date _____

a Demonstrating Proofreading Skills

- Read the paragraph entitled "The Pueblo Indians of the American Southwest: Ancient Cliff Dwellers." The paragraph contains ten errors (punctuation, capitalization, spelling, verb tense, etc.) Circle the errors, then write the corrections in the margins.

The Pueblo Indians of the American Southwest: Ancient Cliff Dwellers

early ancestors of the today's present day pueblo Indians built their

homes on sides of cliffs as early as 1000 B.C. The amazing

architecture of these dwellings continues to astound modern-day

builders. the rooms were generally build under overhangs or in the

sides of cliffs. Multistoried homes were Created from stone building

blocks made of handmade adobe mortar. The homes usually

housed extended families Family members moveed freely through

the homes by using an intricate system off ladders and doorways in

ceilings. Archaeologists believ these homes were built as a defense

against invading tribes. Although it is still a mystery as to why, the

dwellings were abandoned in the early 14th Century?

_____
_____
_____
_____
_____
_____
_____
_____
_____
_____

ELD Standard
   Edit writing for grammatical structures and the mechanics of writing.
ELA Standard
   Demonstrate appropriate English usage.

Name _____   Date _____

b Demonstrating Comprehension: Main Idea and Supporting Details

✔ A good paragraph is written beginning with a clear topic sentence. Topic sentences tell what the paragraph will be about. They contain the main idea. The sentences that follow the topic sentence give more information about the main idea. These sentences contain the supporting details.

Writing Prompts

■ Read each topic sentence. Write three supporting details to go with each one.

Topic sentence: I learned three things about cliff dwellers.

1. _____

2. _____

3. _____

Topic sentence: Egyptian culture is complex and interesting.

1. _____

2. _____

3. _____

Topic sentence: Mayan pyramids are different from Egyptian pyramids.

1. _____

2. _____

3. _____

ELD Standard
    Identify and explain the main ideas and critical details of informational materials, literary texts and texts in content areas.
ELA Standard
    Include the main ideas and most significant details.

69

Name _____   Date _____

a Demonstrating Comprehension

━━ ━━ ━━ ━━ ━━ ━━ ━━ ━━ ━━ ━━ ━━ ━━ ━━ ━━ ━━ ━━ ━━

■ Read the passage below and then answer the questions that follow. Use complete sentences in your answers.

The British Colonies

The first permanent settlement in North America was in 1607. It was the English colony at Jamestown, in what is now the state of Virginia. The Pilgrims followed, and in 1620 they set up a colony at Plymouth, in what is now the state of Massachusetts.

Other English colonies sprang up all along the Atlantic coast, from Maine in the north to Georgia in the south. By the mid-1700s, there were 13 British colonies. They were Massachusetts, New Hampshire, Connecticut, Rhode Island, New York, New Jersey, Pennsylvania, Maryland, Delaware, Virginia, North Carolina, South Carolina, and Georgia.

Many different kinds of people came to the colonies. Some, such as the Quakers, came to the colonies to escape religious persecution. Some came to find riches in the New World. Others were sent to serve out criminal sentences, such as the convicts of Georgia. What they had in common was that they were all looking to start a new life.

Questions:

1. When was the colony at Jamestown established?

   _____

2. Who founded the colony at Plymouth?

   _____

3. How many British colonies were there by the mid-1700s?

   _____

4. Why did the Quakers come to the colonies?

   _____

5. What did all of the colonists have in common?

   _____

ELD Standard
   Write simple sentences of brief responses to selected literature to show factual understanding of the text.
ELA Standard
   Demonstrate alphabet principle.

6. What present-day state was the settlement at Plymouth in?

_____

The 13 Colonies

Massachusetts	Rhode Island	Pennsylvania	Virginia	Georgia
New Hampshire	New York	Maryland	North Carolina	
Connecticut	New Jersey	Delaware	South Carolina	

■ Make a list of the 13 colonies, putting them in alphabetical order.

_____

_____

_____

_____

_____

_____

_____

_____

_____

_____

_____

_____

_____

Name _____   Date _____

b Writing Sentences with the Simple Past Tense

▬▬ ▬ ▬ ▬ ▬▬ ▬▬ ▬ ▬ ▬▬ ▬▬ ▬▬ ▬▬ ▬ ▬▬ ▬▬ ▬▬ ▬▬ ▬▬

✔ The most common way to make a present tense verb into a past tense verb is to add the suffix *ed* to the end:

Example: **follow = followed**

✔ Most verbs follow this rule with the following considerations:

> If the verb ends with the letter *e*: Change the *e* to *ed*:
>
> **guide = guided**

> If the verb's last two letters are a vowel and a consonant: Double the consonant and add *ed*:
>
> **tap = tapped**

> If the verb ends in a consonant and *y*: Drop the *y* and add *ied*:
>
> **study = studied**

> If the verb ends in a vowel and *y*: Add *ed*:
>
> **play = played**

▬▬ ▬ ▬ ▬ ▬▬ ▬▬ ▬ ▬ ▬▬ ▬▬ ▬▬ ▬▬ ▬ ▬▬ ▬▬ ▬▬ ▬▬ ▬▬

■ Use the vocabulary from the box to write five sentences about the first European settlers, using the simple past tense with regular and irregular verbs.

sailing ship	hometown	challenges	church	pray	colonist	board
sail	suffer	storm	worship	arrive	bunk	deck

1. _____

2. _____

3. _____

4. _____

5. _____

ELD Standard
Produce independent writing with consistent use of capitalization, periods, and correct spelling.
ELA Standard
Identify and use regular and irregular past tense verbs.

Name   Date

a Demonstrating Comprehension

■ Read the passage below and complete the sentences with the correct past tense verb in the blanks.

The Slave Trade

In the four hundred years between 1450 and 1850, at least 12 million people from Africa were shipped across the Atlantic Ocean to colonies in North America, South America and the West Indies (the Islands around the Caribbean Sea.) These people were essentially kidnapped and sent against their will to work in the New World. At least 7 million, or 80% of these people were "exported" during the 18th century, with a mortality rate of somewhere between 10-20% on the ships bound for the Americas. Probably at least 4 million Africans also died in slave wars and forced marches before even being sent across the Atlantic Ocean. Many of these people resisted their captors by mutiny on the ships or by jumping overboard during what became known as the *Middle Passage* across the Atlantic Ocean to America.

The African slave trade and consequent slave labor changed the way things worked in the world. In the Americas, slave labor became the essential engine that kept the agricultural economy of the 17th and 18th centuries thriving. The greatest demand for slaves in the Americas came from Brazil and the sugar plantations of the Caribbean. In Brazil, slavery lasted until 1888.

Slavery was abolished in the United States in 1865, after the Civil War. It was officially ended with a Constitutional Amendment. However, the South was largely opposed to this, primarily because the economy of Southern states depended on slave labor.

African slaves and their descendants carried their skills and values, and their rich traditions to cultures around the world.

1. At least 12 million Africans were (to ship) _____ from Africa to the Americas.

2. The African slave trade (to change) _____ the way things worked in the world.

3. Slavery in the United States was (to abolish) _____ in 1865, after the Civil War.

4. Many slaves (to resist) _____ their captors by jumping overboard from slave ships.

5. Probably at least 4 million Africans also (to die) _____ in slave wars and forced marches in Africa before they were shipped to the New World.

6. Slaves and their descendants (to carry) _____ their skills, values and traditions to cultures around the world.

7. Africans were (to kidnap) _____ and sent against their will to work in the New World.

ELD Standard
    Produce independent writing with consistent use of capitalization, periods, and correct spelling.
ELA Standard
    Identify and use regular past tense verbs.

Name _____   Date _____

b Understanding Proper and Common Nouns

▬ ▬ ▬ ▬ ▬ ▬ ▬ ▬ ▬ ▬ ▬ ▬ ▬ ▬ ▬ ▬

✔ A proper noun names a specific person, place, thing, or idea. It always begins with a capital letter.

✔ A common noun names any person, place, thing, or idea. It does not begin with a capital letter.

Examples: The **captain** sailed the ship. (common noun)

General Washington sailed the Delaware River. (proper noun)

▬ ▬ ▬ ▬ ▬ ▬ ▬ ▬ ▬ ▬ ▬ ▬ ▬ ▬ ▬ ▬

■ Using the words from the box below, fill in the following chart. Follow the examples in the first row.

voyage	England	Frederick Douglass
slave	ships	colony
Africa	values	leaders
Harriet Tubman	Brazil	village
freedom	sugar	owners
liberty	Abraham Lincoln	plantation

	Person	Place	Thing	Idea
Common Nouns	slave	village	sugar	values
Proper Nouns	Frederick Douglass	England		

ELD Standard
Use correct parts of speech.
ELA Standard
Identify all parts of speech.

Name _____   Date _____

α Past Progressive Verbs

✔ The tense of a verb shows when the action happened. One way to show that an action happened in the past is to use the simple past tense, which is formed by adding *ed* to the end of the verb. Another way is to use the past progressive tense, which is formed by adding a "helping verb" and *ing* to the end of the verb.

Examples: **was helping**

were making

✔ Rules for adding *ing* to the form the present progressive verb:

Rule	Verb	Add *ing*
For most verbs, add *ing*:	fall	is/are falling
For verbs that end in silent *e*, drop the *e* and add *ing*:	come	is/are coming
For verbs ending with a vowel and consonant, double the consonant and add *ing*:	tap	is/are tapping

■ Complete the chart below to form past progressive verbs. Follow the example.

Verb	Past Progressive Tense
Example: to travel	was traveling
to circle	
to go	
to study	
to repair	

■ Complete the following exercise by filling in the present progressive form of the verb in parenthesis.

Example:

(to leave)   _____ is leaving _____

1. (to camp)   _____

2. (to move)   _____

3. (to explore)   _____

4. (to begin)   _____

5. (to rest)   _____

6. (to hunt)   _____

7. (to cook)   _____

8. (to stop)   _____

ELD Standard
Understand and follow simple written directions for classroom-related activities.
ELA Standard
Identify and use regular and irregular past tense verbs.

Name _____   Date _____

ⓑ Demonstrating Comprehension

▬ ▬ ▬ ▬ ▬ ▬ ▬ ▬ ▬ ▬ ▬ ▬ ▬ ▬ ▬ ▬

■ Complete the sentences below by providing the correct word from the box to complete each sentence.

camped	mountains
adventure	journey
wagons	territories
hunt	communities
settle	rivers
claim	West
travel	

1. The pioneer family began its _____ in the East.

2. The wagons had to travel over tall _____ and cross wide

   _____.

3. They laid a _____ to the land they wanted to

   _____ on.

4. The children hoped that the journey would be a fun _____.

5. They traveled to the new _____ in covered

   _____.

6. They had to _____ for their food as they

   _____ all along the way.

7. Pioneers hoped to form new _____ in the

   _____.

8. It was extremely difficult to _____ across the continent in covered
   wagons.

ELD Standard
   Use correct parts of speech.
ELA Standard
   Identify and correctly use various parts of speech.

Name _____   Date _____

a Possessive Pronouns

✔ A possessive pronoun shows ownership. It tells you that something belongs to someone.

Example: This is **Squanto's** bow.
       This is **his**.

mine ours	yours	his hers its	theirs

■ Write which possessive pronoun you would use in each case.

Example:

the headdress that the Native American man wears: _____his_____

1. the wagon that I have: _____

2. the reservation where the tribe lives: _____

3. the wheel on the wagon: _____

4. the wagons belonging to the settlers: _____

5. the pet dog that the girl has: _____

6. the country where we live: _____

7. the cabin where they live: _____

8. the horse that I own: _____

9. the horns on the goat: _____

10. the dress that the woman bought: _____

ELD Standard
   Identify and use parts of speech.
ELA Standard
   Make clear references between pronouns and antecedents.

Name _____   Date _____

b Possessive Pronouns

▬▬ ▬▬ ▬▬ ▬▬ ▬▬ ▬▬ ▬▬ ▬▬ ▬▬ ▬▬ ▬▬ ▬▬ ▬▬ ▬▬ ▬▬ ▬▬ ▬▬

■ Complete each sentence with the correct possessive pronoun.

1. "Mr. Boone, one of your men left _____ (shovel) on the mountain," said a worker.

2. "This is _____ for the trip west," yelled the worker, as he put his shovel into his pack.

3. "I believe this is _____," said the pioneer, as he handed a shovel to his son.

4. "Are those horses _____?" asked the trail master, pointing to the group of Native Americans.

▬▬ ▬▬ ▬▬ ▬▬ ▬▬ ▬▬ ▬▬ ▬▬ ▬▬ ▬▬ ▬▬ ▬▬ ▬▬ ▬▬ ▬▬ ▬▬ ▬▬

■ Write five sentences using possessive pronouns.

1. _____

2. _____

3. _____

4. _____

5. _____

ELD Standard
   Identify and use parts of speech.
ELA Standard
   Make clear references between pronouns and antecedents.

Name _____   Date _____

a Prepositional Phrases

✔ A prepositional phrase is made up of a preposition and a noun.

PREPOSITIONS

to	in	above	over	of	behind	between
by	at	upon	with	after	under	below

■ Make a list of prepositional phrases, using prepositions from the box above. Then use five of the phrases in complete sentences.

Prepositional phrases:

Example: by horseback

1. _____   6. _____

2. _____   7. _____

3. _____   8. _____

4. _____   9. _____

5. _____   10. _____

Sentences:

Example: The doctor traveled <u>by horseback</u> to visit.

1. _____

2. _____

3. _____

4. _____

5. _____

ELD Standard
Use clauses, phrases, and mechanics of writing with consistent variations in grammatical forms.
ELA Standard
Demonstrate mechanics of writing and appropriate English usage.

79

Name _____   Date _____

b Writing an Informative Paragraph

▬▬ ▬ ▬ ▬ ▬ ▬ ▬ ▬▬ ▬▬ ▬ ▬ ▬▬ ▬▬ ▬ ▬▬ ▬

■ Select one of the topics listed below and write an informative paragraph about it. Write your paragraph in the past tense. Remember to begin with a topic sentence that states the main idea, and to provide supporting details. You may want to use encyclopedias or online search engines to research your topic.

Topics:

Harriet Tubman

The Abolitionist Movement

Frederick Douglass

The Fugitive Slave Bill of 1850

the book *Uncle Tom's Cabin*

Abraham Lincoln

_____
(Title)

_____

_____

_____

_____

_____

_____

_____

_____

_____

_____

ELD Standard
    Proceed through the writing process to write short paragraphs that contain supporting details about a given topic.
ELA Standard
    Include the main ideas and most significant details.

Name _____   Date _____

ⓐ Writing a Postcard

■ Read the postcards and answer the questions about them.

Postcard from 1849

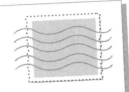

July 9, 1849

Dear Aunt Mary,

We arrived in California after a long trip. Everyone is ok, but the baby was sick for a week. Dad has found a job and we think we have a place to live.

Write to us soon. We miss all our family and friends, but we are full of hope about our new life.

Love, Henry

Mary L. Johnsen
18 Main Street
Park Town, Virginia

1. Who wrote this postcard?

_____

2. When was it written?

_____

3. Who received it?

_____

4. Where is Henry?

_____

Postcard from 2004

7/3/04

Dear Mac:

Haven't heard from you in ages! How've you been? Did you get my package last month? I hope you liked your present!

Can you come to visit this summer? I really hope so. Write back soon or send me an e-mail.

Sam

Mac Martinez
39 Rice Court
Los Angeles, CA 91344

1. Where does Mac Martinez live?

_____

2. What is Sam hoping?

_____

3. Who is writing this postcard?

_____

4. When was this postcard written?

_____

ELD Standard
   Use common verbs, nouns, and high-frequency modifiers in writing simple sentences.
ELA Standard
   Demonstrate appropriate English usage.

81

Name _____   Date _____

ⓑ Demonstrating Comprehension

■ Read each postcard below written by Gold Rush Era "Forty Niners." Then answer the questions that go with each one using complete sentences.

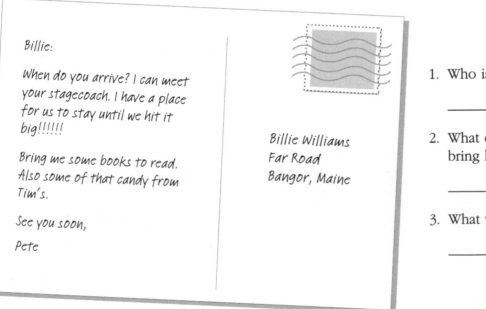

Dear Ma:

I'm having a lot of luck here in Calif. I got a room in a boarding house and have even found some nuggets of gold! I just know that I'll find a lot more! When I do I'll send you something pretty.

Your Willie

Mrs. Blatt
10 Elm St.
Boston, Mass.

1. Who is Willie writing to?

_____

2. Where is Willie staying?

_____

3. What will Willie do after he finds a lot more gold?

_____

4. What street does Mrs. Blatt live on?

_____

Billie:

When do you arrive? I can meet your stagecoach. I have a place for us to stay until we hit it big!!!!!!

Bring me some books to read. Also some of that candy from Tim's.

See you soon,

Pete

Billie Williams
Far Road
Bangor, Maine

1. Who is coming to see Pete?

_____

2. What does Pete want Billie to bring him from Maine?

_____

3. What will Billie be traveling on?

_____

ELD Standard
Use common verbs, nouns, and high-frequency modifiers in writing simple sentences.
ELA Standard
Demonstrate appropriate English usage.

Dear Rev. Lynch:

How is everything back home? I am homesick. I don't know if I will stay here looking for gold much longer. Life is very hard and I am running out of money. Give my best to Mrs. Lynch.

Sincerely,

T.R. Smith

Rev. Paul Lynch
11 Main St.
Richmond, Virginia

1. How is T.R. Smith feeling about life in California?

_____

2. Who is T.R. Smith writing to?

_____

3. Where does Rev. Paul Lynch live?

_____

Name _____   Date _____

a Proper Adjectives

━━ ━━ ━━ ━━ ━━ ━━ ━━ ━━ ━━ ━━ ━━ ━━ ━━ ━━ ━━ ━━

✔ Remember that proper nouns name specific people or places. Adjectives describe people, places, things, or ideas. Proper adjectives <u>describe</u> a specific person or place.

Example: **The doctor came to our house.**

The Polish doctor came to our house. (proper adjective)

━━ ━━ ━━ ━━ ━━ ━━ ━━ ━━ ━━ ━━ ━━ ━━ ━━ ━━ ━━ ━━

■ Rewrite each sentence below, providing the correct proper adjective in each blank space.

Example:

I sent a letter to my (from Spain) _____ Spanish _____ friend.

1. The (from England) _____ boat set sail for America.

2. The (from Mexico) _____ lullaby put the baby to sleep.

3. The new boy in class is (from Russia) _____.

4. There were five (from America) _____ on the tour of the landmark.

5. The (from Persia) _____ rug cannot go on the boat because of shipping rules.

6. The (from France) _____ Prime Minister will be arriving at the airport tomorrow morning.

7. My aunt brought me a beautiful (from Germany) _____ clock.

━━ ━━ ━━ ━━ ━━ ━━ ━━ ━━ ━━ ━━ ━━ ━━ ━━ ━━ ━━ ━━

■ Write ten more proper adjectives:

1. _____   6. _____

2. _____   7. _____

3. _____   8. _____

4. _____   9. _____

5. _____   10. _____

ELD Standard
    Identify and use parts of speech.
ELA Standard
    Identify and use adjectives correctly.

Name _____   Date _____

b Demonstrating Comprehension

▪ Read the following interview of an immigrant family from Eastern Europe, being interviewed by an immigration official in the year 1900. Then answer the questions about the interview.

Interviewer: What is your complete name?
Immigrant: Aleksander Majewski.

Interviewer: What country did you come from?
Immigrant: Poland.

Interviewer: What language(s) do you speak?
Immigrant: Polish and a little of English.

Interviewer: What kind of work did you do in your country?
Immigrant: I was a carpenter. I built tables and chairs.

Interviewer: Why did you leave your country to come to America?
Immigrant: We were poor and there was not enough work for me to feed my family.

Interviewer: How many people are there in your family?
Immigrant: My wife, my three children and me.

Interviewer: How was your trip across the Atlantic Ocean?
Immigrant: It was hard. We were on a large boat with many people. Some were sick.

Interviewer: Do you have any medical problems?
Immigrant: No. But my youngest child has some problems with a cough.

Interviewer: Do you have any relatives or family members living in America? If so, where do they live?
Immigrant: Yes, my two brothers live here in New York City.

Questions:

1. What country does this immigrant come from?

   _____

2. What is this immigrant's last name?

   _____

3. What kind of work did Mr. Majewski do in Poland?

   _____

ELD Standard
   Respond to comprehension questions about text by using detailed sentences.
ELA Standard
   Demonstrate comprehension by identifying answers in the text.

4. Where do this man's two brothers live?

_____

5. What languages does Mr. Majewski speak?

_____

6. Do any of the people in this family have medical problems?

_____

Name _____   Date _____

▣ Identifying Types of Sentences

▬ ▬ ▬ ▬ ▬ ▬ ▬ ▬ ▬ ▬ ▬ ▬ ▬ ▬ ▬ ▬ ▬ ▬ ▬ ▬

✔ There are three types of sentences: declarative, interrogative, and exclamatory. A declarative sentence gives information and ends with a period. An interrogative sentence asks a question and ends with a question mark. An exclamatory sentence is a strong emotional phrase and ends with an exclamation point.

Example: **Chinese immigrants suffered from racial prejudice in America.** (declarative)

Why did the Chinese continue to arrive in California? (interrogative)

This is unfair treatment! (exclamatory)

▬ ▬ ▬ ▬ ▬ ▬ ▬ ▬ ▬ ▬ ▬ ▬ ▬ ▬ ▬ ▬ ▬ ▬ ▬ ▬

■ Read the sentences below and classify them based on whether they are declarative, interrogative, or exclamatory. Write next to the sentence a *D* if it is a declarative sentence, *I* if it is an interrogative sentence, and *E* if it is an exclamatory sentence.

1. Immigrants from the Province of Guangdong in Southern China began immigrating to the United States to escape a collapsed economic system. _____

2. Welcome! _____

3. Why did the U.S. economy take a downturn in the early 1870s? _____

4. Why were the Chinese blamed for the economic problems when they really did not play a role in them? _____

5. Local politicians of the time used the anti-Chinese sentiment to fuel their own career goals. _____

6. The people shouted, "Justice for all!" _____

7. Have you ever met a Polish person? _____

8. Many Japanese and Chinese immigrants came to the United States in the early 1900s. _____

9. Where did your ancestors come from? _____

10. What a beautiful beach! _____

ELD Standard
Identify basic vocabulary, mechanics, and sentence structures in a piece of writing.
ELA Standard
Identify types and structure of sentences.

87

Name   Date

b Main Idea and Supporting Details

■ Read each paragraph. Then complete the exercises by filling in the main ideas and supporting details.

Asian immigrants were treated poorly during the late 1880s. Prejudice towards the Chinese led to rude and, sometimes, inhumane treatment of these immigrants. Legislation was passed in 1882 called the Chinese Exclusion Act, which made it difficult for Chinese immigrants to come to the United States. Many Chinese immigrants living in the United States at the time were not able to bring their families from China. As a result, most Chinese neighborhoods were made up of bachelors who worked and sent money back home to their families.

Main idea: _____

_____

Supporting details:

_____

_____

_____

_____

Prejudice towards Asians by the citizens and government of the United States grew worse during the early 1900s. This hostility resulted in many Asian immigrants being held as "prisoners" at the Angel Island Immigration Station. Many men, women, and children were held up on this island near San Francisco, California for years, with no hope of getting to the mainland to lead normal lives. They lived in horrible conditions that included inedible food, isolation from mainland families and the separation of families based on gender and age, plus lengthy interrogations.

Main idea: _____

_____

Supporting details:

_____

_____

_____

_____

ELD Standard
Identify and explain the main ideas and critical details of information materials, literary texts, and texts in content areas.
ELA Standard
Distinguish the main idea and supporting details in expository text.

Name _____ Date _____

ⓐ Future Tense

━ ━

✔ The future tense tells about an action that will happen in the future. Using the helping verbs *will* or *going + verb infinitive* with a present tense verb makes verb future tense.

━ ━

■ Use eight of the verbs from the box in sentences using the future tense. Circle all the words making up the future tense verb form in the sentences.

move	relocate	drive	pack	work
migrate	leave	travel	resettle	study

Example: _____ My family (will travel) to the South this summer. _____

1. _____

2. _____

3. _____

4. _____

5. _____

6. _____

7. _____

8. _____

ELD Standard
   Produce independent writing with consistent use of capitalization and periods, and correct spelling.
ELA Standard
   Identify and use future tense verbs.

Name _____   Date _____

b Demonstrating Comprehension

■ Read the passage about the Great Migration. Then answer the questions that follow by marking the correct answer to each question.

The Great Migration

Even though slavery had ended decades before, by the 1890s many black people in the South didn't feel that much had really improved. They were still seriously economically disadvantaged. The laws known as "Jim Crow" made it legal for blacks and whites to have separate facilities in restaurants, hotels and other public places. This came to be known as "separate-but-equal." Blacks were also prevented from voting by such means as charging poll taxes, restricting voting to literate people and only allowing property owners to vote.

Beginning in the 1890s and lasting into the 1970s, a "Great Migration" of black people from the South began. They left for the North and later, the West of the United States, seeking greater opportunity in employment, and more racial equality. The vast majority of these migrants settled in Northern cities such as Chicago, Cleveland, Detroit, Pittsburgh and New York.

The first large wave of migration took place around World War I, when European immigration had slowed down and left the North in need of factory workers. The second large wave began at the end of the Great Depression and the beginning of World War II. At this stage, destinations also included the cities on the West Coast. The Great Migration was the largest movement of people within the United States in its entire history.

1. "Jim Crow" made it legal for —
   - ☐ black people to attend college.
   - ☐ blacks and whites to have separate public facilities.
   - ☐ factory workers to work in the North.

2. The Great Migration began around —
   - ☐ 1970.
   - ☐ 1790.
   - ☐ 1890.

ELD Standard
Generate and respond to questions related to text.
ELA Standard
Demonstrate comprehension by identifying answers in the text.

3. Black people left the South —
   - [ ] seeking greater employment opportunities.
   - [ ] mainly to go on vacation.
   - [ ] but quickly returned.

4. Legal segregation of public places came to be known as —
   - [ ] The Great Migration.
   - [ ] "separate-but-equal".
   - [ ] northern cities.

5. Blacks were prevented from voting —
   - [ ] by the Great Migration.
   - [ ] by poll taxes.
   - [ ] very rarely.

6. The Great Migration —
   - [ ] was the largest movement of people within the United States in its history.
   - [ ] was when many black Americans moved from the North to the South.
   - [ ] ended before World War II.

7. Migrants mainly settled in cities such as —
   - [ ] Montgomery, Mobile, and Atlanta.
   - [ ] Dallas, Baton Rouge, and New Orleans.
   - [ ] New York, Detroit, and Chicago.

Name   Date

ⒶWriting an Essay

■ Write a two-paragraph essay on the Great Migration based on what you read in the previous lesson. Be sure to use topic sentences at the beginning of each paragraph, and to provide supporting details within the paragraphs.

The Great Migration

ELD Standard
    Proceed through the writing process to write short paragraphs that contain supporting details about a given topic.
ELA Standard
    Include the main ideas and most significant details.

Name   Date

b Capitalization

✔ Eras and periods in history that have special names are capitalized.

■ Rewrite the following sentences about different historical periods or events using correct capitalization.

Example:

More than six million Jewish people were killed in the holocaust.
More than six million Jewish people were killed in the **Holocaust**.

1. The cold war officially ended in 1991.

   _____

2. My grandfather lost everything during the stock market crash.

   _____

3. California's population increased dramatically during the gold rush.

   _____

4. During the middle ages, the majority of peasants were farmers.

   _____

5. We fought world war II in Europe and in the Pacific.

   _____

6. The first persian gulf war was from January 16, 1991 to April 6, 1991.

   _____

7. The renaissance took place in European culture during the 15th and 16th Centuries and embodied values of the modern world.

   _____

   _____

8. The colonies gained independence through the american revolution.

   _____

ELD Standard
    Edit writing for basic conventions.
ELA Standard
    Use correct capitalization.

Name _____   Date _____

a Subject–Verb Agreement

- ✔ The verb must agree with the subject of a sentence.
- ✔ If the subject of a sentence is a *singular noun* or *he*, *she*, or *it*, the verb must be *singular*.
- ✔ If the subject is a *plural noun* or *I*, *we*, *you*, or *they*, the verb must be *plural*.
- ✔ <u>Rule</u>: If the subject ends in *s*, the verb *cannot* end in *s*, and if the verb ends in *s*, the subject *cannot* end in *s*.
- ✔ <u>Exception</u>: If the subject is singular and ends in *s*, such as *kiss*, the verb *cannot* end in *s*.

■ Select the correct verb that agrees with the subject of each sentence. Check the correct answer.

1. Some lawyers _____ their clients in court.

   ❑ defends   ❑ defend

2. Do paralegals _____ as long as attorneys do?

   ❑ study   ❑ studies

3. The flag _____ in every courtroom.

   ❑ hangs   ❑ hang

4. The evidence against the defendant _____ not convincing.

   ❑ were   ❑ was

5. The judges _____ from courtroom to courtroom.

   ❑ moves   ❑ move

6. The specialists _____ to discuss the difficult case.

   ❑ meets   ❑ meet

ELD Standard
Use correct parts of speech, including correct subject-verb agreement.
ELA Standard
Identify and use subject and verb correctly.

■ Do the following sentences have correct subject-verb agreement? Check the correct column to indicate *yes* or *no*.

	Yes	No
1. Judges <u>wear</u> black robes.	_____	_____
2. The witnesses <u>testifies</u> during the trial.	_____	_____
3. The attorney <u>discuss</u> details with her partner.	_____	_____
4. The judge <u>listens</u> to all the evidence.	_____	_____
5. Did the investigators <u>contact</u> the police?	_____	_____

Name _____   Date _____

b Alphabetizing/Using Vocabulary in Sentences

■ Put the vocabulary words from the box in alphabetical order. Then use each one in complete sentences.

prosecuting	victim	judge	paralegal	defense
legal	evidence	law	attorney	paramedic
courtroom	police	specialist	crime	emergency

1. _____

_____

2. _____

_____

3. _____

_____

4. _____

_____

5. _____

_____

6. _____

_____

7. _____

_____

8. _____

_____

9. _____

_____

ELD Standard
    Arrange words in alphabetical order.
ELA Standard
    Demonstrate the mechanics of writing and appropriate English usage.

10. _____

_____

11. _____

_____

12. _____

_____

13. _____

_____

14. _____

_____

15. _____

_____

Name _____   Date _____

a Phrasal Verbs

✔ *Phrasal verbs* are words made up of two or more words, where one is the main verb and the other word or words are usually prepositions.

■ Underline the phrasal verb in each sentence.

1. The camera snapped on with a loud click.

2. The police searched for the suspect.

3. The sound boomed across the auditorium.

4. The reporter ran through the rain.

5. The newspaper flew off the press!

6. The lawyers gathered around the judge's bench.

7. The witness moved toward the witness stand.

8. The editor picked out the best story of the day.

9. The child clung to his father's leg.

■ Provide a preposition from the box to complete each phrasal verb below, as in the example.

out	until	without	about	behind	off

Example:

step _____out_____

1. wait _____   4. turn _____

2. do _____   5. pick _____

3. hide _____   6. read _____

ELD Standard
   Use clauses, phrases, and mechanics of writing with consistent variations in grammatical forms.
ELA Standard
   Identify all parts of speech.

Name   Date

b Writing a Numbered List

■ Read the list of topics from the following box. Choose two and write numbered lists describing the steps involved in each activity, using declarative sentences.

| how to make a sandwich | how to plant a plant | how to cook an egg |
| how to wash and dry a dish | how to feed a pet | how to set the table |

Topic #1

1. _____

2. _____

3. _____

4. _____

5. _____

6. _____

7. _____

8. _____

9. _____

10. _____

Topic #2

1. _____

2. _____

3. _____

4. _____

5. _____

ELD Standard
   Produce independent writing with consistent use of capitalization and periods, and correct spelling.
ELA Standard
   Identify types and structures of sentences.

6. _____

7. _____

8. _____

9. _____

10. _____

Name _____   Date _____

a Modal Verbs

▬▬ ▬▬ ▬▬ ▬▬ ▬▬ ▬▬ ▬▬ ▬▬ ▬▬ ▬▬ ▬▬ ▬▬

✔ Some modal verbs are verbs that are followed by the infinitive form of the main verb in a sentence, for example: *Judges* **have** *to wear black robes in court.*

✔ Other modals are followed by the simple form of the verb; for example: *You* **should** *know your rights as a citizen.*

▬▬ ▬▬ ▬▬ ▬▬ ▬▬ ▬▬ ▬▬ ▬▬ ▬▬ ▬▬ ▬▬ ▬▬

■ Underline the modals in each of the following sentences.

1. I need to find a good English tutor.

2. I ought to study two hours every evening.

3. I can read one book a week.

4. I must tell the lawyer what I saw.

5. You should let your teacher know if you're going to be absent.

6. He must learn a lot of material before the test.

7. I can practice my English with several friends from school.

8. She will testify in the civil trial next week.

9. You need to write an article for the school newspaper.

10. I have to go home early tomorrow.

▬▬ ▬▬ ▬▬ ▬▬ ▬▬ ▬▬ ▬▬ ▬▬ ▬▬ ▬▬ ▬▬ ▬▬

■ Complete each sentence by filling in the blank spaces with modal verbs.

1. He _____ to write a long article about voting.

2. I _____ attend the special lecture next Friday.

3. You _____ always tell your parents where you will be.

4. My mother _____ to testify in a court case.

5. Patricia _____ find books for you in the library.

6. Dr. Contreras _____ to see his patient in the hospital.

ELD Standard
   Use correct parts of speech.
ELA Standard
   Identify and use infinitives.

Name _____   Date _____

b Writing Informative Paragraphs

■ Write two informative paragraphs on the topics of your choice. You may also select topics from those in the box. Each paragraph should be at least four sentences long and include a topic sentence.

Describe what paramedics do.	What are ambulances for?
Describe a fire truck.	Describe what happens at hospitals.
Describe how police officers work with dogs.	Describe what firefighters do.

Paragraph #1

Title: _____

_____

_____

_____

_____

_____

_____

_____

_____

Paragraph #2

Title: _____

_____

_____

_____

_____

_____

_____

_____

_____

_____

ELD Standard
Proceed through the writing process to write short paragraphs that contain support details about a given topic.
ELA Standard
Convey clear and accurate perspectives on the subject.

Name _____   Date _____

a Adverbs Ending in -ly

--- --- --- --- --- --- --- --- --- --- --- --- --- --- --- --- --- --- ---

✔ Adverbs describe how an action is done: how fast, how often, etc. Many adverbs end in -ly, and most come after the verb.

✔ Exception: If a verb is followed by an object, the adverb comes *after* the object.

--- --- --- --- --- --- --- --- --- --- --- --- --- --- --- --- --- --- ---

▪ Write the adverb in each sentence on the line provided.

Example:

The ambulance drove quickly through the intersection. _____**quickly**_____

1. I spoke softly while I was in the library. _____

2. Maria walked sadly to the car after her team lost the game. _____

3. The doctor talked frequently to her nurse. _____

4. The paramedic listened carefully to the patient's heart. _____

5. Check her condition immediately! _____

6. When I get nervous my pulse rate increases suddenly. _____

7. After the class, I talked to the teacher privately. _____

8. The entire experience affected me very positively. _____

--- --- --- --- --- --- --- --- --- --- --- --- --- --- --- --- --- --- ---

▪ Read the list of adverbs in the box. Then use five of them in complete sentences.

peacefully	angrily	selfishly	thoughtlessly
silently	repeatedly	loudly	wildly
happily	joyfully	calmly	confidently

1. _____

2. _____

3. _____

ELD Standard
    Identify and use parts of speech.
ELA Standard
    Spell suffixes correctly.

103

4. _____

5. _____

■ Choose four adverbs from the previous box and illustrate them.

Adverb: _____

Adverb: _____

Adverb: _____

Adverb: _____

Name _____   Date _____

b Demonstrating Comprehension

━━ ━━ ━━ ━━ ━━ ━━ ━━ ━━ ━━ ━━ ━━ ━━ ━━ ━━ ━━ ━━ ━━

■ Read the following passages on the medical field. Then answer the questions that follow by marking the correct answer.

If you get an ear infection, sometimes your doctor will give you an antibiotic to cure it. When you are prescribed an antibiotic, it is extremely important to take the medicine until it is gone, even if your ear stops hurting and you think your infection is gone. If you don't finish taking the medicine, the infection might return and your ear could once again begin hurting.

The main idea of this passage is:

☐ ear infections hurt

☐ if you get an ear infection your doctor might give you an antibiotic

☐ you should finish all the medicine your doctor gives you

Smoking is one of the very worst things people can do to their bodies. Even so, each day almost 5,000 kids and teenagers smoke for the first time. Tobacco companies spend billions of dollars every year on ads to try to make kids buy cigarettes because new smokers keep them in business! But cigarettes are extremely bad for you. They lead to many health problems and can even cause cancer. They are addictive, expensive, and dangerous. It is best to never start smoking!

What is the main idea of this passage?

_____

_____

_____

Microscopes are powerful magnifying glasses. They allow us to see things that are too small to see with just our eyes. Looking through a microscope, you can see the cells of your body or what is in a drop of your blood. By using a microscope to see these things up close, a doctor can find cancer or harmful bacteria, as many other problems that could cause serious illness.

1. What do microscopes allow us to do?

_____

_____

_____

ELD Standard
   Identify and explain the main ideas and critical details of informational materials, literary texts, and texts in content areas.
ELA Standard
   Demonstrate comprehension by identifying answers in the text.

105

2. What can you see through a microscope?

_____

_____

_____

3. What can doctors discover by using a microscope?

_____

_____

_____

Name _____   Date _____

a Action Verbs/Subject–Verb Agreement

━━ ━━ ━━ ━━ ━━ ━━ ━━ ━━ ━━ ━━ ━━ ━━ ━━ ━━ ━━

✔ Remember that action verbs tell what the subject does.

━━ ━━ ━━ ━━ ━━ ━━ ━━ ━━ ━━ ━━ ━━ ━━ ━━ ━━ ━━

■ Write the correct action verb in each sentence. Then read the sentences to a partner.

1. The farm worker _____ grapes during harvest. (pick/picks)

2. Does the farmer _____ his own tractor? (drive/drives)

3. The grower _____ the lettuce at the Farmers' Market. (sell/sells)

4. How many tons of almonds do they _____? (produce/produces)

5. Pedro _____ a tractor at the vineyard. (drive/drives)

6. The grocer _____ cauliflower, broccoli, cabbage and tomatoes. (display/displays)

7. The farm workers _____ heads of lettuce into cartons. (puts/put)

8. Did the farmer _____ fertilizer into the bucket? (pour/pours)

9. Trucks _____ along the highway at all hours of the day. (run/runs)

━━ ━━ ━━ ━━ ━━ ━━ ━━ ━━ ━━ ━━ ━━ ━━ ━━ ━━ ━━

grow/grows	produce/produces	drive/drives	pick/picks
farm/farms	harvest/harvests	plant/plants	sell/sells

■ Choose four words from the box and use them in sentences. Be sure to pay attention to subject-verb agreement.

1. _____

2. _____

3. _____

4. _____

ELD Standard
Use correct parts of speech, including correct subject-verb agreement.
ELA Standard
Identify and use subject and verb correctly.

107

Name _____   Date _____

b Demonstrating Comprehension

▪ Read the passage and answer the questions by checking the correct answer. Then underline or highlight all of the action verbs in the passage.

"The People's Department"

The "People's Department" was the name that President Lincoln gave to the U. S. Department of Agriculture. In 1862, when he founded the USDA, 58% of the population of the United States were farmers and 90% made at least some of their income from farming. They needed good information and good seeds for growing the nation's food. In 1889, the Department of Agriculture became a part of the president's cabinet.

Today the USDA has an expanded role. It is responsible for the safety of meat, poultry, and egg products. Consumers benefit from USDA research, which helps ensure the quality and safety of our high-quality food supply. Twenty five million schoolchildren eat school lunches each day, and millions of Americans also receive food stamps to help feed their families in time of need.

The USDA is also the steward of 192 million acres of our national forests and rangelands, and it is the country's largest conservation agency, encouraging efforts to protect soil, water, and wildlife. The USDA serves the American people in diverse ways, and it continues to be the "People's Department."

1. Who founded the USDA?
   - [ ] George Washington
   - [ ] Abraham Lincoln
   - [ ] Theodore Roosevelt

2. How many schoolchildren get school lunches every day?
   - [ ] 25 thousand
   - [ ] 25 hundred
   - [ ] 25 million

3. What did people need from the USDA in 1862?
   - [ ] food stamps
   - [ ] forest protection
   - [ ] good seeds

4. Now, the USDA is part of the president's —
   - [ ] agency.
   - [ ] department.
   - [ ] cabinet.

5. As a conservation agency, the USDA protects —
   - [ ] soil and water.
   - [ ] the president's cabinet.
   - [ ] research.

6. Abraham Lincoln founded the USDA in —
   - [ ] 1999.
   - [ ] 1862.
   - [ ] 1889.

ELD Standard
Generate and respond to questions related to text.
ELA Standard
Identify all parts of speech.

Name _____   Date _____

ⓐ Homonyms

━━ ━━ ━━ ━━ ━━ ━━ ━━ ━━ ━━ ━━ ━━ ━━ ━━ ━━ ━━ ━━ ━━ ━━

✔ Homonyms are pairs of words that sound the same but have different spellings and different meanings.

━━ ━━ ━━ ━━ ━━ ━━ ━━ ━━ ━━ ━━ ━━ ━━ ━━ ━━ ━━ ━━ ━━ ━━

■ Read the sentences below. Choose and write the correct word that completes each sentence. You may want to use a dictionary to help you complete this exercise.

1. The _____ looked at us with big, brown eyes. (doe/dough)

2. Did you mark the _____ box on the form? (write/right)

3. By the _____, what did you say your name was? (way/weigh)

4. I bumped my baby _____ on a chair and now it really hurts! (tow/toe)

5. I always prefer to sit on the _____ in the theater. (I'll/aisle)

6. Pilar is going to Spain to visit her _____ next July. (ant/aunt)

7. She's glad that everyone has next _____ off! (week/weak)

8. Becca's father served in the military during the _____. (war/wore)

9. Franklin's ancestors came from _____. (whales/Wales)

10. Everyone knows that it is impolite to _____ at people. (stare/stair)

11. The children hope for _____ around the world. (peace/piece)

12. Marta's parents stayed at an _____ by the ocean. (in/inn)

13. We only had one _____ to prepare for our oral report. (our/hour)

14. Don't forget to say _____ to my old friend when you see him. (high/hi)

15. Did you just get your _____ cut? (hare/hair)

16. Roberto sent Fabiano a _____. (fax/facts)

ELD Standard
Use a standard dictionary to determine meaning of unknown words.
ELA Standard
Clarify word meanings through the use of definition, example, restatement, or contrast.

Name _____   Date _____

b Parts of Speech: Nouns and Verbs

▬ ▬ ▬ ▬ ▬ ▬ ▬ ▬ ▬ ▬ ▬ ▬ ▬ ▬ ▬ ▬ ▬ ▬

✔ Certain words can be verbs or nouns, depending upon how they are used.

▬ ▬ ▬ ▬ ▬ ▬ ▬ ▬ ▬ ▬ ▬ ▬ ▬ ▬ ▬ ▬ ▬ ▬

■ Read the following sentences. Decide whether the underlined word is used as a verb or a noun. Write *verb* or *noun* on the line provided.

1. You need to <u>brush</u> you hair!   _____

2. What time is it according to your <u>watch</u>?   _____

3. It's never a good idea to tell a <u>lie</u>.   _____

4. Did you <u>cover</u> the computer before you left?   _____

5. I <u>regret</u> that I didn't study harder for the exam.   _____

6. Can you see the <u>cross</u> on top of the church?   _____

7. Will you pay a <u>visit</u> to Manuel in the hospital?   _____

8. You need a <u>permit</u> to park your car there.   _____

9. Jose said he'll <u>pay</u> me back tomorrow.   _____

10. The principal tried to <u>silence</u> the students.   _____

11. I only have one <u>wish</u> regarding my future.   _____

12. Did you <u>curl</u> your hair today?   _____

ELD Standard
    Identify and use parts of speech.
ELA Standard
    Identify all parts of speech.

Name _____   Date _____

ⓐ Habitual Present Tense

✔ The habitual present tense of a verb is used to tell about things that are done on a regular basis. They aren't necessarily happening now, but they happen all the time.

Example: **The factory worker <u>builds</u> cars.**

■ Use the present tense of the verb in parenthesis to complete the following sentences in the habitual present tense.

1. The engineer _____ the plans before building begins. (to review)

2. As a farmer, Juan _____ the fields after every harvest. (to plow)

3. The gardener _____ the hedges once a month. (to trim)

4. That paramedic _____ many lives each year! (to save)

5. Our neighbor is a firefighter that _____ fires and also works as a paramedic. (to fight)

6. That lawyer _____ people accused of crimes. (to defend)

7. My beautician _____ my hair once a month. (to style)

8. Jorge is a barber who always _____ his customers. (to shave)

9. Which judge _____ the best decisions? (to make)

10. Your grocer _____ the produce so beautifully! (to arrange)

11. Sofia is a farm worker who _____ almonds. (to harvest)

12. The pianist from Miami _____ gorgeous music! (to play)

ELD Standard
  Edit writing for basic conventions.
ELA Standard
  Demonstrate appropriate English usage.

111

Name   Date
_____   _____

b Suffixes

▬▬ ▬▬ ▬ ▬▬ ▬ ▬▬ ▬ ▬▬ ▬ ▬▬ ▬ ▬▬ ▬ ▬▬ ▬ ▬▬ ▬ ▬▬ ▬ ▬▬

✔ By adding the suffix *-er* to a noun, you can create the name of a job or describe the kind of work a person does.

✔ Other suffixes that are used in the same way are *-ist* and *-or*.

▬▬ ▬▬ ▬ ▬▬ ▬ ▬▬ ▬ ▬▬ ▬ ▬▬ ▬ ▬▬ ▬ ▬▬ ▬ ▬▬ ▬ ▬▬ ▬ ▬▬

■ Look at each picture below and write the job name for each, adding the correct suffix. Underline the suffix in each word you write.

_____   _____   _____   _____

▬▬ ▬▬ ▬ ▬▬ ▬ ▬▬ ▬ ▬▬ ▬ ▬▬ ▬ ▬▬ ▬ ▬▬ ▬ ▬▬ ▬ ▬▬ ▬ ▬▬

■ Write a sentence using each word below. In each sentence, include information about what the job is like, or what the person does at work.

1. (doctor) _____

2. (hairstylist) _____

3. (engineer) _____

4. (writer) _____

5. (designer) _____

6. (photographer) _____

ELD Standard
Apply knowledge of word relationships, such as roots and affixes.
ELA Standard
Spell correctly roots, inflections, suffixes and prefixes, and syllable constructions.

Name _____   Date _____

ⓐ The Impersonal *You*

━━ ━━ ━━ ━━ ━━ ━━ ━━ ━━ ━━ ━━ ━━ ━━ ━━ ━━ ━━ ━━ ━━

✔ The pronoun *you* is sometimes used to talk about people *in general*.

━━ ━━ ━━ ━━ ━━ ━━ ━━ ━━ ━━ ━━ ━━ ━━ ━━ ━━ ━━ ━━ ━━

▪ Finish each question by using the impersonal *you* and information from the unit about sales and retail. Use the vocabulary words from the box to complete the sentences. Underline the word *you* in each sentence.

produce	clerk	receipt	credit card	agent
sales	customers	percentage	cashier	

Example: **If you don't want to pay with cash or a check, (credit card) _you_ can use a credit card.**

1. When you want to buy a house, (agent)

   _____

2. If you need to return something to a store, (receipt)

   _____

3. When you want to make a salad, (produce)

   _____

4. To figure out how much the tax is on a purchase, (percentage)

   _____

5. If you would like to work at a store, (sales)

   _____

6. When you need help finding something at a shop, (clerk)

   _____

7. When the store is having a sale, (customers)

   _____

8. When it's time to pay for your merchandise, (cashier)

   _____

ELD Standard
  Identify and use parts of speech.
ELA Standard
  Identify all parts of speech.

Name _____   Date _____

b Demonstrating Comprehension: Want Ads

▪ Read the following examples of want ads. Then answer the questions that follow. Use complete sentences, when required.

Wanted: Receptionist for small medical office

Requirements: High school diploma
Bilingual: English/Spanish
Good phone skills

Other desired qualities: Good writer, ability to keep office organized, good "people skills"

30 hours/week
Salary negotiable
Call 669–0021 between 4–7 p.m.

---

1. What level of education do you need for this job?

   _____

2. What kind of job is this?

   _____

3. What are some of the qualities that this employer is looking for? (check 2)
   - [ ] a person can work 40 hours a week
   - [ ] a person who writes well
   - [ ] someone who doesn't earn too much
   - [ ] good skills working with people

Help Wanted: Hard-working person to work at counter of busy sandwich shop! /
Fun work for someone who likes people!/ $7.50/hour/ Monday-Friday 10:00–4:00/
Interested? Call: 503–677–7781

---

4. If you got this job, you would be working _____.

5. What are the hours of this job? _____

6. How do you apply for this job? _____

ELD Standard
Complete simple informational documents related to career development.
ELA Standard
Understand and analyze the differences in structure and purpose between various categories of informational materials.

Name _____   Date _____

a Writing an Interview

- Read the following text of a job interview with a partner.

I = Interviewer
C = Job Candidate

I #1: Welcome. My name is Sandra Wilson.

I #2: Hello, I'm Joe Chin.

C: Hi. My name is Manny Fernandez.

I #1: You have applied to work in the Men's Department here in our store. Have you ever worked in a store before?

C: Yes, last summer I worked in a department store in the mall.

I #2: What did you do there?

C: I worked in the shoe section. I helped people by getting them their correct shoe size. I also worked at the cash register.

I #1: Did you enjoy that job? Tell us what you liked about it.

C: Yes, very much. I like working with people. Also, since I can speak Spanish and English, I can help lots of people. I really enjoy talking to different kinds of people. I got very good at working the register, too.

I #2: Manny, are you available to work on weekends?

C: Yes. I could work then, also during the week.

I #1: You seem to have the skills we are looking for. So we'd like to offer you the job, beginning next week, at $10.00 an hour.

C: Great! Thank you for the interview.

ELD Standard
    Complete simple informational documents related to career development.
ELA Standard
    Demonstrate the mechanics of writing and appropriate English usage.

■ Write a job interview with a partner. Use one of the ads from the previous lesson to find some information to start with. The possible candidate will not have experience, but he/she is eager to learn.

_____

_____

_____

_____

_____

_____

_____

_____

_____

_____

_____

_____

_____

_____

_____

_____

_____

_____

_____

_____

_____

_____

_____

_____

Name _____   Date _____

b Demonstrating Comprehension

■ Answer the following questions about the job interview by marking the correct answer.

1. What is the name of the person who is interviewing for the job?
   - ☐ Joe
   - ☐ Sandra
   - ☐ Manny
   - ☐ Wilson

2. Where did the job candidate work last summer?
   - ☐ at a restaurant
   - ☐ at a bank
   - ☐ at a school
   - ☐ at a department store

3. What is one of Manny's special skills?
   - ☐ He is very good at math.
   - ☐ He speaks two languages.
   - ☐ He likes it at the mall.

4. What is Interviewer #1's name?
   - ☐ Manny Fernandez
   - ☐ Sandra Wilson
   - ☐ Joe Chin

5. How much money will Manny be making?
   - ☐ $10.00 per hour
   - ☐ $7.50 per hour
   - ☐ $150.00 per week

6. What department did Manny work in the summer before?
   - ☐ the Men's Department
   - ☐ the shoe department
   - ☐ the credit department
   - ☐ the candy department

7. Does Manny already know how to operate a cash register?
   - ☐ Yes.
   - ☐ No.
   - ☐ The interviewer doesn't say.
   - ☐ Manny doesn't say.

ELD Standard
   Generate and respond to questions related to text.
ELA Standard
   Demonstrate comprehension by identifying answers in the text.

117

Name _____   Date _____

▣ Adverbs of Time

▬ ▬

✔ **Simple past tense**: Used to express action that took place in the past or a condition that existed at a definite time in the past.

✔ **Present progressive tense**: Used to express an action happening at the present moment.

✔ **Future tense**: Used to indicate action in the future.

✔ **Some adverbs of time**: yesterday, tomorrow, next week, today, now, next year, last year, last week.

▬ ▬

■ Complete each sentence by filling in the correct tense of the missing word, as in the example.

Example:

Next year my brother _____will build_____ a wooden chair. (to build)

1. Yesterday the carpenter _____ a cabinet for the new kitchen. (to build)

2. Next year the plumber _____ the pipes in our bathroom. (to repair)

3. Last week the electrician _____ the new house down the block. (to wire)

4. Tomorrow the construction workers _____ the construction site. (to clean)

5. Today my neighbor _____ his shower. (to replace)

6. Now I _____ the dimensions of my living room floor so I can get new carpet. (to measure)

7. Last year my grandfather _____ a new bathtub and sink in his condominium. (to install)

ELD Standard
    Identify and use parts of speech.
ELA Standard
    Identify all parts of speech.

Name _____   Date _____

b Writing an Essay

- Choose a job to write about. After you have taken notes on the duties of the job, how that worker interacts with others, etc., write your three-paragraph essay in the space below.

Notes

Job title: _____

_____

_____

_____

_____

_____

_____

_____

_____

_____

_____

_____

_____

_____

_____

ELD Standard
Write expository compositions, such as descriptions, comparisons and contrast, and problem and solution, that include a main idea and some details in simple sentences.
ELA Standard
Use strategies of notetaking, outlining, and summarizing, to impose structure on composition drafts.

Name _____   Date _____

ⓐ Demonstrating Comprehension

■ Read the following chart with a partner. Then complete the sentences by selecting the correct answer option, based on the information from the chart and what you might already know about the solar system.

Planet	Orbit	Diameter (in Miles)
Mercury	88 Earth days	3,031
Venus	225 Earth days	7,521
Earth	365 days	7,926
Mars	1.88 Earth years	4,217
Jupiter	11.86 Earth years	88,850
Saturn	29.5 Earth years	74,901
Uranus	84 Earth years	31,765
Neptune	164.8 Earth years	30,777
Pluto	248.5 Earth years	1,429

Example:

The diameter of Jupiter is ___88,850 miles___.
- ☐ 11.86 Earth years
- ☐ 4,217 miles
- ☑ 88,850 miles
- ☐ 1.88 Earth years

1. Saturn's orbit is _____.
- ☐ shorter than Mercury's orbit
- ☐ longer than Neptune's orbit
- ☐ 74,901 miles
- ☐ shorter than Earth's orbit

2. Mars's diameter is _____.
- ☐ greater than Jupiter's
- ☐ greater than Pluto's
- ☐ 3,031 miles
- ☐ smaller than Mercury's

3. Neptune's diameter is _____.
- ☐ far greater than Jupiter's
- ☐ roughly the same as that of Mars
- ☐ roughly the same as that of Uranus
- ☐ the smallest of any planet

ELD Standard
Understand and follow simple written directions for classroom–related activities.
ELA Standard
Understand how text features make information accessible and usable.

4. The Earth is the only planet _____.
   - [ ] known as the rocky planet
   - [ ] with a red atmosphere
   - [ ] known to support life
   - [ ] that is a gas giant

5. The last planet in our solar system to be discovered was _____.
   - [ ] Uranus
   - [ ] Pluto
   - [ ] Jupiter
   - [ ] Neptune

6. The planet closest to the Sun is _____.
   - [ ] Venus
   - [ ] Earth
   - [ ] Mercury
   - [ ] Saturn

7. The planet best known for its rings is _____.
   - [ ] Pluto
   - [ ] Mars
   - [ ] Neptune
   - [ ] Saturn

Name _____   Date _____

b Comparatives/Superlatives/Ordinal Numbers

✔ Comparatives and superlatives are used to compare things.

✔ Ordinal numbers express sequence or degree.

Examples: **Saturn is** *larger than* **Venus.** (comparative)

Jupiter is *the largest* **planet in our solar system.** (superlative)

Venus is the *second* **planet from the Sun.** (ordinal)

■ Write or complete the sentences below using words from the box. Follow the prompt at the beginning or end of each line.

solar system	Neptune	Uranus	farthest	smaller	fifth
planet	Venus	diameter	closest	first	sixth
Earth	Pluto	miles	larger	second	seventh
Sun	Jupiter	orbit	largest	third	eighth
Mercury	Saturn	years	smallest	fourth	

1. _____ (comparative sentence)

2. _____ (sentence with ordinal number)

3. _____ (superlative sentence)

4. Mercury is _____ Earth. (comparative)

5. Jupiter is _____ Pluto. (comparative)

6. Pluto is _____ planet in the solar system. (superlative)

7. Jupiter is _____ planet in the solar system. (superlative)

8. Mercury is _____ planet to the Sun. (superlative)

9. Pluto is _____ planet from the Sun. (superlative)

10. Uranus is the _____ planet from the Sun. (ordinal)

11. Earth is the _____ planet from the Sun. (ordinal)

12. Venus is the _____ planet from the Sun. (ordinal)

ELD Standard
Understand and follow simple written directions for classroom-related activities.
ELA Standard
Identify types and structure of sentences.

Name _____   Date _____

a Present Tense: Statements of Fact

▬ ▬ ▬ ▬ ▬ ▬ ▬ ▬ ▬ ▬ ▬ ▬ ▬ ▬ ▬ ▬ ▬ ▬ ▬ ▬

✔ The present tense is used to make statements of fact, as well as to tell about habitual actions or routines.

Example: **The Sun is five billion years old.** (fact)

▬ ▬ ▬ ▬ ▬ ▬ ▬ ▬ ▬ ▬ ▬ ▬ ▬ ▬ ▬ ▬ ▬ ▬ ▬ ▬

■ The words in the box below relate to the Sun and energy. Write statements that express facts on the lines provided, making sure to use the present tense of the verb. You may want to consult an encyclopedia or science textbook to help you with this exercise. After writing the sentences, illustrate them with colored pencils or markers.

corona	star	radiation	helium	gas	prominences
hydrogen	sunspots	atomic particles	nuclear fusion	eclipse	energy

Fact #1 _____

Fact #2 _____

Fact #3 _____

Fact #4 _____

Fact #5 _____

1	2	3

4	5

ELD Standard
Collect information from various sources and take notes on a given topic.
ELA Standard
Identify types and structure of sentences.

123

Name _____   Date _____

b Predicate Adjectives

✔ Adjectives modify nouns: they tell what kind, how many or which one.

✔ Adjectives usually come before nouns, but *predicate adjectives* follow a *linking verb* and modify the subject.

Example: *The dog is* friendly; *The students are* intelligent.

■ Read the following incomplete sentences about the Sun. Then complete each sentence below by writing a predicate adjective in the blank space. Use an encyclopedia or dictionary to find the information to complete the exercise, if necessary.

1. The Sun looks _____ in the sky.

2. The Earth's atmosphere is _____.

3. The temperature of the Sun is _____.

4. Some stars are _____. (color)

5. Solar coronas are _____.

■ Circle the predicate adjective in each sentence.

1. The particles that escape from the corona are tiny.

2. Prominences are loops of gas that are huge.

3. Some of the planets in the solar system are rocky.

4. Part of the surface of the Sun is granulated.

5. The hottest stars are blue and the coolest are red.

ELD Standard
    Identify and use parts of speech.
ELA Standard
    Identify all parts of speech.

Name _____   Date _____

a There Is/There Are

▬ ▬ ▬ ▬ ▬ ▬ ▬ ▬ ▬ ▬ ▬ ▬ ▬ ▬ ▬ ▬ ▬ ▬

✔ The words *there is* and *there are* are used to talk about the existence of something.
✔ *There is* is used with uncountable nouns and singular nouns.
✔ *There are* is used with plural nouns.

▬ ▬ ▬ ▬ ▬ ▬ ▬ ▬ ▬ ▬ ▬ ▬ ▬ ▬ ▬ ▬ ▬ ▬

■ Fill in the words *There is* or *There are* in each sentence. On the line following each sentence, indicate whether the sentence has an uncountable noun, a singular noun, or a plural noun.

Example:

_____There is_____ a small inner core in the Moon.

_____singular noun_____

1. _____ many phases of the Moon.

   _____

2. _____ no water on the Moon.

   _____

3. _____ mainly solid rock on the Moon.

   _____

4. _____ numerous craters on the Moon.

   _____

5. _____ a crater named Julius Caesar on the Moon.

   _____

6. _____ a thinner crust on the near side of the Moon than on the far side.

   _____

7. _____ a lot of dust on the surface of the Moon.

   _____

8. _____ crater walls that are thousands of feet high.

   _____

ELD Standard
Use correct parts of speech, including correct subject-verb agreement.
ELA Standard
Demonstrate appropriate English usage.

Name _____   Date _____

b Demonstrating Comprehension

■ Read the Peruvian folktale, "The Fox in the Moon," below. It tells why Peruvians see a fox in the full moon to this day. Answer the comprehension questions that follow, using complete sentences.

The Fox in the Moon

Fox came to talk with Mole as he was digging for worms. Mole asked him what he wanted most in the world, and Fox said he wanted to go to the Moon. All he needed to do was figure out a way to get there.

As Fox was running through some grass, an idea came to him: what if he took some grass and made a very long rope, so he could climb it up to the Moon. He ran back to Mole and told him all about his idea.

So the two friends braided grass by the light of the moon every night, watching as their rope grew and grew. One night, anxious to be finished with their rope, Fox took it and twirled it over his head, as he tried to lasso the Moon. As the rope came thumping back down, Fox noticed Eagle nearby. Eagle agreed to fly the rope to the Moon and hitch it up for the two friends.

The next night, after Eagle had taken the rope, Fox tugged at the rope and it didn't fall to the Earth—it stayed put! Fox began climbing first, followed by Mole. Fox made it to the Moon, but Mole slipped and was rescued by Eagle, just in the nick of time.

To this day, Fox can still be seen as he was on the Moon, and Mole remains so embarrassed that he only comes out of his tunnel after dark.

1. What does Fox want to do more than anything in the world?

   _____

2. What idea does Fox come up with to get to the Moon?

   _____

3. What did Fox and Mole do with the grass?

   _____

4. How did the two friends finally get the rope up to the Moon?

   _____

ELD Standard
   Write simple sentences of brief responses to selected literature to show factual understanding of the text.
ELA Standard
   Analyze characterization as delineated through a character's thoughts, words, speech patterns, and actions; the narrator's description'
   and the thoughts, words, and actions of other characters.

5. What happened to Mole when he tried to climb the rope?

_____

6. What happened to Fox when he tried to climb the rope?

_____

7. Why do you think people in Peru still see a fox in the full moon?

_____

Name _____   Date _____

α Compound Sentences

✔ Conjunctions are words that connect two sentences to form a compound sentence. The most common conjunctions are *and* and *but*. Use *and* when you want to connect two like ideas together. Use *but* when there is a difference between the two ideas.

■ Read the two sentences, then combine them into one sentence, using the conjunctions *and* or *but*, depending on the information.

Examples:

Mars is hot. Mercury is very hot

Mars is hot, **but** Mercury is hotter.

1. From a distance, Mars has a red surface. From a distance, Earth has a blue and white surface.

_____

2. Earth has volcanoes. Mars has volcanoes.

_____

3. Earth has one moon. Mars has two moons.

_____

4. Mars has riverbeds on its surface. Earth has riverbeds on its surface.

_____

5. Spacecraft from Earth have landed on Mars. Spacecraft from Earth haven't landed on either of Mars's moons.

_____

_____

6. Earth has polar caps. Mars has polar caps.

_____

ELD Standard
    Edit and correct basic grammatical structures and usage of the conventions of writing.
ELA Standard
    Use conjunctions to connect ideas.

■ Write five sentences of your own, combining two sentences into one sentence, using the conjunctions *and* or *but*, depending on the information you use.

1. _____

2. _____

3. _____

4. _____

5. _____

Name _____　　　　　　Date _____

b Adjectives

✔ Adjectives modify nouns. They tell *how much*, *what kind*, and *how many*.

■ Read the following statements about the planet Mars. Find the adjective(s) in each sentence and circle it (them).

1. There are several extinct volcanoes on Mars.

2. Mars has two tiny moons, Deimos and Phobos.

3. The channels on Mars's surface were probably caused by flowing water.

4. The large plains on parts of Mars's surface are made up of solidified volcanic lava.

5. The fine dust on Mars gets whipped up into dust storms.

6. Mars is known as the Red Planet.

7. There is red, iron-rich dust on Mars.

8. Mars also has clouds of frozen carbon dioxide.

9. Mars has a solid, rocky crust.

10. The surface of Mars has morning mists.

■ Think of other adjectives that describe Mars, or other planets you have studied so far, and write them on the lines below, along with nouns they modify.

_____

_____

_____

_____

_____

_____

ELD Standard
　　Identify and use parts of speech.
ELA Standard
　　Identify all parts of speech.

Name _____   Date _____

a Adjectives with Commas

▬ ▬ ▬ ▬ ▬ ▬ ▬ ▬ ▬ ▬ ▬ ▬ ▬ ▬ ▬ ▬ ▬ ▬

✔ Commas are used to separate more than two adjectives when the comma could be replaced with the word *and*. The adjectives all need to modify the same noun.

▬ ▬ ▬ ▬ ▬ ▬ ▬ ▬ ▬ ▬ ▬ ▬ ▬ ▬ ▬ ▬ ▬ ▬

■ Rewrite the sentences below, placing commas between the adjectives, as in the example.

Example:

From Earth, the Moon looks bumpy and white and round.

From Earth, the Moon looks bumpy, white, and round.
_____

1. Jupiter's moon, Europa, is smooth and icy and cracked.

_____

2. Jupiter has one faint and thin principal ring.

_____

3. Io is covered with bright red and orange and yellow splotches.

_____

4. Jupiter's zones are bright and cool and high.

_____

5. The surface of the Moon is completely silent and still and dusty.

_____

6. Stars can be blue and red and yellow.

_____

▬ ▬ ▬ ▬ ▬ ▬ ▬ ▬ ▬ ▬ ▬ ▬ ▬ ▬ ▬ ▬ ▬ ▬

■ Write three sentences using adjectives separated by commas.

1. _____

2. _____

3. _____

ELD Standard
    Edit and correct basic grammatical structures and usage of the conventions of writing.
ELA Standard
    Use commas for items in a series.

131

Name _____   Date _____

b Synonyms and Antonyms

━ ━ ━ ━ ━ ━ ━ ━ ━ ━ ━ ━ ━ ━ ━ ━ ━ ━ ━

✔ *Synonyms* are words that have the same meaning.

✔ *Antonyms* are words that have the opposite meaning.

━ ━ ━ ━ ━ ━ ━ ━ ━ ━ ━ ━ ━ ━ ━ ━ ━ ━ ━

■ For each of the two sections, *Synonyms* and *Antonyms*, select the correct answer and mark it with a ✔.

Synonyms	**Antonyms**
1. burst	1. smooth
☐ burn	☐ lined
☐ explode	☐ rough
☐ throw	☐ square
2. glow	2. liquid
☐ shine	☐ drink
☐ frown	☐ baked
☐ extinguish	☐ solid
3. outer	3. dark
☐ middle	☐ black
☐ interior	☐ light
☐ exterior	☐ white
4. amount	4. shrink
☐ count	☐ expand
☐ subtract	☐ iron
☐ quantity	☐ dry
5. tiny	5. tiny
☐ enormous	☐ medium
☐ miniature	☐ miniscule
☐ timely	☐ big
6. silence	6. silent
☐ quiet	☐ noisy
☐ chaos	☐ quiet
☐ whisper	☐ whisper

132

ELD Standard
Recognize simple antonyms and synonyms in written text. Expand recognition of them and begin to use appropriately.
ELA Standard
Understand and explain common antonyms and synonyms.

Name _____   Date _____

α Vocabulary: Greek and Latin Roots

■ Match the planet name from the column on the left with the Greek or Roman god from which it got its name. Draw a line between the two.

Neptune   Lord of the underworld

Saturn   Lord of the sea

Jupiter   Goddess of love

Mercury   Ruler of the world

Mars   Ruler of all the gods

Uranus   God of war

Venus   Messenger of the gods

Pluto   God of farming

■ Write a complete sentence about each of the planets below.

1. Saturn

   _____

2. Jupiter

   _____

3. Earth

   _____

4. Mars

   _____

ELD Standard
    Produce independent writing with consistent use of capitalization and periods, and correct spelling.
ELA Standard
    Use knowledge of Greek, Latin, and Anglo-Saxon roots and affixes to understand content-area vocabulary.

133

Name _____   Date _____

b Comparing and Contrasting

■ Read the two passages below, one about Neptune and one about Pluto. Then fill in the chart with information about how the two are alike and how they are different.

Neptune

Neptune is one of the two farthest planets from the Earth. Occasionally it is the outermost planet when Pluto passes inside its orbit. It is a gas giant. Neptune has eight moons and four rings. It contains an icy mantle. Neptune's core is made of icy water, ammonia and methane. Neptune is enormous and much is known about it.

Pluto

Pluto is also one of the two farthest planets from the Earth. It is usually the outermost planet, but sometimes passes inside Neptune's orbit. It is a rocky planet. Pluto has only one moon and no known rings. It has an icy mantle. Pluto's core is made of rock and possibly ice. Pluto is so small and far away that little is known about it.

	How Neptune and Pluto are alike	How Neptune and Pluto are different
Distance from Earth		
General description of planet		
Moons, rings, and other features		
Planet core		
General size and knowledge about planet		

What conclusion can you draw about the characteristics of Neptune and Pluto, based on the above chart?

_____

_____

ELD Standard
Write simple compositions, such as descriptions and comparison and contrast, that have a main idea and some detail.
ELA Standard
Compare and contrast information on the same topic after reading several passages or articles.

Name _____   Date _____

a Simple Definitions

■ Use a dictionary to find simple definitions for the following words relating to meteors, asteroids and comets. Write the definition next to the word.

1. orbit: _____

2. gravity: _____

3. crater: _____

4. celestial: _____

5. meteor shower: _____

6. meteoroid: _____

7. nucleus: _____

■ Use an encyclopedia to look up the following terms. Write a short definition in the space provided.

1. Oort Cloud: _____

2. shooting star: _____

3. Leonid meteor shower: _____

4. Halley's Comet: _____

ELD Standard
Use a standard dictionary to determine the meaning of unknown words.
ELA Standard
Use a dictionary to learn the meaning and other features of unknown words.

135

Name   Date

b Demonstrating Comprehension

▬ ▬ ▬ ▬ ▬ ▬ ▬ ▬ ▬ ▬ ▬ ▬ ▬ ▬ ▬ ▬ ▬ ▬

■ Read the paragraph below and answer the questions that follow by marking the correct answer option.

Meteors, asteroids and comets are often thought to be alike because they are all free-flying pieces of debris in space. In reality, they differ from each other in many ways. Comets are lumps of ice and dust that come from somewhere in a huge cloud that surrounds the solar system. Asteroids are small, rocky objects with irregular shapes, most of which orbit the Sun in the asteroid belt (between the orbits of Mars and Jupiter.) They may be left over from the beginning of the solar system. They travel at high speeds and sometimes pieces of them break off. These rock pieces, as well as chunks of comets, can become meteoroids. Meteors are what meteoroids are called when they fall into the Earth's atmosphere. They become heated by friction and look like a glowing streak. These are called "shooting stars." Meteoroids are small chunks of stone-like or metal-like debris traveling in outer space. Most are no larger than a pebble. Although most of the "falling stars" burn up before they reach Earth, any leftover piece that does reach Earth is called a meteorite. Meteorites can make holes or craters when they hit the Earth.

1. What do asteroids, comets and meteoroids have in common?
   ☐ They all fall to Earth and make craters.
   ☐ They all are no larger than a pebble.
   ☐ They are all pieces of debris in space.
   ☐ They are all huge clouds of gas.

2. How would you describe a comet?
   ☐ chunks of stone-like debris
   ☐ a gas tail
   ☐ lumps of ice and dust
   ☐ a hole or crater in the Earth

3. What are meteors?
   ☐ gases that originate in a huge cloud
   ☐ the surfaces of comets
   ☐ debris in the asteroid belt
   ☐ meteorites that are entering Earth's atmosphere

4. Asteroids orbit the Sun —
   ☐ between the orbits of Mars and Jupiter.
   ☐ between the orbits of Mars and Earth.
   ☐ very rarely.
   ☐ as heat vapor.

5. What is a "shooting star?"
   ☐ an asteroid
   ☐ a meteor
   ☐ a comet
   ☐ none of the above

ELD Standard
Generate and respond to questions related to text.
ELA Standard
Demonstrate comprehension by identifying answers in the text.

Name   Date
_____   _____

ⓐ Greek and Latin Roots

▬ ▬ ▬ ▬ ▬ ▬ ▬ ▬ ▬ ▬ ▬ ▬ ▬ ▬ ▬ ▬ ▬ ▬ ▬

✔ Many words in English contain Greek and Latin roots. These roots have specific meanings and can be built upon to create new words related to the meaning.

  Example: *bios* (Greek) = life

    Words: biology, biography, biomass, biosphere

▬ ▬ ▬ ▬ ▬ ▬ ▬ ▬ ▬ ▬ ▬ ▬ ▬ ▬ ▬ ▬ ▬ ▬ ▬

■ Read the words under each Greek or Latin root. In the box, provide words that are derived from the same root. You may want to use a dictionary for this exercise. Then choose one word from each box, write down its meaning, and use it in a complete sentence.

Hydro (Greek) = water

_____   _____   _____   _____

Nephele (Greek) = cloud

_____   _____   _____   _____

Terra (Latin) = earth

_____   _____   _____   _____

Lumen (Latin) = light

_____   _____   _____   _____

Okeanus (Greek) = Oceanus (Latin) the outer sea

_____   _____   _____   _____

Lunaris – Luna (Latin) = the moon

_____   _____   _____   _____

ELD Standard
    Apply knowledge of word relationships, such as roots and affixes, to derive meaning from literature and content areas.
ELA Standard
    Use knowledge of Greek, Latin, and Anglo-Saxon roots and affixes to understand content-area vocabulary.

1. **Word**: _____ **Meaning**: _____

_____

2. **Word**: _____ **Meaning**: _____

_____

3. **Word**: _____ **Meaning**: _____

_____

4. **Word**: _____ **Meaning**: _____

_____

5. **Word**: _____ **Meaning**: _____

_____

6. **Word**: _____ **Meaning**: _____

_____

Name   Date
_____   _____

b Punctuation: Titles

✔ Titles of books are always italicized, and if they are handwritten, they are underlined.

✔ Titles of magazines and newspapers are also italicized.

✔ The titles of articles within magazines and newspapers are punctuated with quotation marks.

Example: The first book I read on the topic of space was Our Solar System.

Correct: The first book I read on the topic of space was *Our Solar System*.

■ Read the sentences below and fill in all the necessary punctuation. Highlight all the titles that need italics.

1. Have you read the book Find the Constellations by H. A. Rey.

   _____

2. No, but I read Meteor by Patricia Polacco.

   _____

3. I found a good article called Stars and Dust in an astronomy magazine.

   _____

4. I got a subscription to Astronomy Today Magazine for my birthday.

   _____

5. I ordered The Sun by Seymour Simon from the book order.

   _____

6. The entire class read the article in the newspaper entitled Telescopes.

   _____

7. My favorite article in National Geographic was about Saturn and I believe it was called The Ringed Planet.

   _____

   _____

8. My homework is to read the book Destination: Jupiter by next Friday.

   _____

ELD Standard
   Edit writing for basic conventions.
ELA Standard
   Use underlining, quotations marks, or italics to identify titles of documents.

139

Name _____   Date _____

a Suffixes

▬▬ ▬▬ ▬▬ ▬▬ ▬▬ ▬▬ ▬▬ ▬▬ ▬▬ ▬▬ ▬▬ ▬▬ ▬▬ ▬▬

✔ A suffix is a word part that is added on to the end of the word.

✔ Suffixes determine whether a word is an adjective, adverb, verb, or noun.

▬▬ ▬▬ ▬▬ ▬▬ ▬▬ ▬▬ ▬▬ ▬▬ ▬▬ ▬▬ ▬▬ ▬▬ ▬▬ ▬▬

■ Read each suffix and its meaning in the following chart. Then find examples of words that contain each suffix and write one of them in the spaces provided. Illustrate the chosen word from each group.

Suffix	Meaning
-ward	toward a specified place, position or time
-er, -or	agent, one who
-ology	the study of
-ing	the action of

Suffix	Meaning
-en	made of, to make
-ist	a person who does
-itis	inflammation of
-scope	instrument for seeing

Word: _____

Word: _____

Word: _____

Word: _____

Word: _____

Word: _____

Word: _____

Word: _____

▬▬ ▬▬ ▬▬ ▬▬ ▬▬ ▬▬ ▬▬ ▬▬ ▬▬ ▬▬ ▬▬ ▬▬ ▬▬ ▬▬

■ Find two other suffixes. Tell what they mean and find several examples of each. Write all of this information on the lines below.

_____

_____

_____

ELD Standard
    Apply knowledge of word relationships, such as roots and affixes, to derive meaning from literature and in texts in content area.
ELA Standard
    Use knowledge of prefixes and suffixes to determine the meaning of words.

Name _____   Date _____

b Proper Nouns

✔ The names of galaxies, constellations, comets, meteors, and stars are proper nouns. As with other proper nouns, they always need to be capitalized.

Example: Milky Way Galaxy

■ Read each term and decide whether it should be capitalized or not. If the term is correct, write an **X** in the second column. If it is incorrect, write it correctly in the third column.

Word	Word is Correct as Written	Corrected Spelling of Word
andromeda galaxy		
southern sky		
galaxy		
halley's comet		
supernova		
corona		
north pole		
callisto		
black hole		
big bang theory		
rosette nebula		
sagittarius		
atmosphere		
magnetic field		

ELD Standard
    Edit writing for basic conventions.
ELA Standard
    Use correct capitalization.

141

Name _____   Date _____

a Prefixes

▬ ▬ ▬ ▬ ▬ ▬ ▬ ▬ ▬ ▬ ▬ ▬ ▬ ▬ ▬ ▬ ▬

✔ A prefix is a letter, or letters, put in front of a root word that change the meaning of the word.

Prefix	Meaning	Prefix + Root Word
pre-	before	preheat
re-	repeat	repay
mis-	not	misbehaving
un-	undo / not	unafraid

■ Add prefixes to base words and write new words in the boxes.

anti-, *ant-* meaning: against, opposite

_____

_____

_____

micro- meaning: small

_____

_____

_____

inter-, *intro-* meaning: between

_____

_____

_____

bene- meaning: good, well

_____

_____

_____

trans- meaning: across

_____

_____

_____

sub- meaning: under, below

_____

_____

_____

ELD Standard
    Recognize simple affixes, prefixes, synonyms, and antonyms.
ELA Standard
    Use knowledge of prefixes and suffixes to determine the meaning of words.

Name _____   Date _____

b Writing a Research Report

■ Select one of the space missions below and write a research report about it. Use the Writing Checklist to help you organize your report.

Gemini	Voyager	Mir	Mars Odyssey
Mars Pathfinder	Apollo	Cassini	Genesis
Mercury	Hubble	Magellan	Galileo

Space mission: _____

_____

_____

_____

_____

_____

_____

_____

_____

_____

_____

_____

_____

_____

_____

_____

_____

_____

_____

_____

ELD Standard
  Create a draft of a paragraph by following an outline.
ELA Standard
  Use strategies of notetaking, outlining, and summarizing to impose structure on composition drafts.

Name _____   Date _____

a Serial Commas

✔ You use the serial comma to separate three or more nouns listed in a row. You separate the nouns with commas, putting the word *and* before the final noun.

Example: The sink has dirty bowls and plates and spoons.
The sink has dirty bowls, plates, __and__ spoons.

■ Rewrite the following sentences, placing commas between the nouns in the sentences below.

1. We had to buy a refrigerator and a microwave and a stove and a toaster.

_____

2. Please put the knives and forks and spoons in the drawer.

_____

3. You need to cut up the peppers and onions and garlic and tomatoes.

_____

4. Grandmother plans to make spaghetti and chicken and tamales and salad for the party on Sunday.

_____

5. Ramona and Freddie got a coffee pot and a waffle iron and a toaster oven for their wedding.

_____

6. Our neighbor bakes pies and cakes and cookies and brownies and tarts.

_____

■ Write sentences using the serial comma with the sets of words provided, as in the example.

Example:

pot, pan, spoon

_____ I got ready to cook by getting out the pots, pans, and spoons.

1. rice, beans, lettuce

_____

ELD Standard
    Edit writing for basic conventions.
ELA Standard
    Use commas for items in a series.

2. cauliflower, broccoli, zucchini

_____

3. mix, stir, blend

_____

4. wash, rinse, dry

_____

5. cinnamon, vanilla, sugar, chocolate

_____

6. towel, sponge, dish soap, dish drainer

_____

Name _____   Date _____

b Compound Sentences

———

✔ When you combine two sentences with a conjunction, you get a compound sentence. The conjunction *and* is used for complementary ideas while the conjunction *but* is used for contrasting ideas.

Examples: **The larger spoons are used for soup, and the smaller spoons are used for coffee.** (complementary ideas)

The dining room is large, but the kitchen is very small. (contrasting ideas)

———

■ Complete the following sentences. Pay special attention to the conjunctions, as they will signal whether the missing clause will be a complimentary idea or a contrasting idea.

1. Maria's kitchen is extremely modern, but _____

   _____

2. My grandmother's utensils are silver, but _____

   _____

3. I always prefer cooking on a gas stove, and _____

   _____

4. I use my blender to make sauce, and _____

   _____

5. I would have turned on the fan, but _____

   _____

———

■ Provide the appropriate conjunction (*and* or *but*) in the following sentences.

1. Pablo has an all-white kitchen, _____ Luisa has a brown wooden kitchen.

2. Carolina enjoys cooking, _____ her best friend enjoys it, too.

3. Our math teacher wants to take a cooking class, _____ her husband wants to study Italian.

4. Roberto's school has a modern kitchen for students, _____ Luis's school still needs to build a new facility.

ELD Standard
   Use more complex vocabulary and sentences appropriate for language arts and other content areas.
ELA Standard
   Use simple and compound sentences in writing and speaking.

Name   Date

a Compound Nouns

✔ A compound noun is a word made up of two words put together.

Example: grand + mother = grandmother

■ Combine the two words to create a new compound word. Write the new word in the box on the right.

Word 1	Word 2	Compound Word		Word 1	Word 2	Compound Word
race	horse			farm	house	
saw	horse			hand	ball	
hand	bag			dish	washer	

■ Draw a line from a word in the left column to a word in the right column, forming a compound word. Then draw and label three of the new words in the boxes provided.

honey	track
arrow	snake
card	head
paper	beat
rattle	moon
dish	pot
clergy	washer
race	board
heart	man
coffee	back

1	2	3

Name _____   Date _____

b Forming Compound Sentences

▬ ▬ ▬ ▬ ▬ ▬ ▬ ▬ ▬ ▬ ▬ ▬ ▬ ▬ ▬ ▬ ▬ ▬ ▬ ▬

✔ Conjunctions are words that connect words, phrases, or clauses.

✔ When you combine two sentences to form a compound sentence, sometimes you need to change parts of the sentence to avoid repetition.

▬ ▬ ▬ ▬ ▬ ▬ ▬ ▬ ▬ ▬ ▬ ▬ ▬ ▬ ▬ ▬ ▬ ▬ ▬ ▬

■ Write compound sentences by combining the two sentences with a conjunction.

Example:

The box cutter is sharp. The drill is sharp.

The box cutter **and** drill are sharp.

1. The handsaw was expensive, but the saw wasn't. The drill was expensive, but the level wasn't.

   _____

2. The pliers were in the toolbox, and the screwdriver was on the bench. The hammer was in the toolbox, and the ruler was on the bench.

   _____

   _____

3. Juan Manuel spends a lot of time in his workshop. Marcos is always in his garden.

   _____

4. The first thing you learn in shop is how to use a power saw. The first thing you learn in cooking class is how to use the stove.

   _____

   _____

5. I inherited a level and saw from my granddad. I inherited a power drill from my uncle.

   _____

6. I love the chairs you made in your workshop! I don't particularly like the table I made in my garage!

   _____

   _____

ELD Standard
   Use more complex vocabulary and sentences appropriate for language arts and other content areas.
ELA Standard
   Use simple and compound sentences in writing and speaking.

7. My brother wants to study carpentry. My sister wants to study welding.

_____

■ Read the sentences below. Decide whether or not each one is a compound sentence, and check the appropriate box in the columns.

	Yes	No
1. Decide whether you want to build a birdhouse, a dollhouse, or a little chair!	❏	❏
2. Mr. Perera teaches electrical shop, but Mr. Smith teaches wood shop.	❏	❏
3. The carpenter has a clock and a chalkboard hanging on the wall of his workshop.	❏	❏
4. I need to buy lumber today, and I also need to get some sandpaper.	❏	❏

Name   Date

a Idioms

✔ An idiom is an expression that has a different meaning from the literal meaning of each word. These expressions have to be memorized by speakers of other languages, since they can't be understood simply by using logic.

Example: *Don't bug me!* Literally, this expression doesn't make any sense. Its meaning is *Don't bother me*, and it should be memorized.

■ Read the idiomatic expressions below. Select the most accurate meaning of the idiom by checking the appropriate box.

1. *You scratch my back, and I'll scratch yours!*
   ☐ If you give me a massage, I'll be happy.
   ☐ If you do something to help me, I'll do something to help you.
   ☐ Don't bother me.

2. *That is so cool!*
   ☐ I really like this cold weather!
   ☐ It's really hot, but I'm saying it's cold!
   ☐ That is wonderful!

3. *Give me five!*
   ☐ Slap my hand in congratulations!
   ☐ I need five minutes to calm myself down!
   ☐ Give me five dollars!

4. *Give me a break!*
   ☐ I need to take a break and relax!
   ☐ Don't be ridiculous!
   ☐ Break off a piece of that food for me.

5. *You're pulling my leg!*
   ☐ You are yanking on my leg to bother me!
   ☐ You are kidding me!
   ☐ You're insulting me!

6. *It's raining cats and dogs!*
   ☐ It's pouring down rain.
   ☐ There are too many cats outside.
   ☐ The cats and dogs are all mixed together.

7. *She went back to face the music.*
   ☐ She returned to practice the piano.
   ☐ She faced the orchestra as she conducted the song.
   ☐ She went back to accept the consequences.

8. *My grandmother is fit as a fiddle.*
   ☐ My grandmother plays the violin.
   ☐ My grandmother is distracted.
   ☐ My grandmother is in very good health.

ELD Standard
Use common idioms, and some analogies and metaphors.
ELA Standard
Identify idioms.

151

■ Draw four of the previous idioms, using the literal meanings. Try to make them as humorous as you can.

Idiom: _____

Idiom: _____

Idiom: _____

Idiom: _____

Name _____   Date _____

b Proverbs

— —

✔ Proverbs are traditional sayings that people always say the same way. They express an obvious truth or some common wisdom. They vary from culture to culture.

✔ An idiom is just a phrase. It can be used in many different kinds of sentences.

Example: *Finders keepers, losers weepers.* This proverb means that the people who find things are lucky, but the people who lose things are out of luck!

> It is always best to tell the truth.
>
> You can get a lot more accomplished if you get up early in the morning.
>
> The person who gets there first gets waited on first.
>
> Don't be critical of something you get for free.
>
> It is a lot easier to accomplish things if people work together.
>
> It is a good idea to maintain some privacy.
>
> It isn't worthwhile to have regrets.
>
> You can come up with really good ideas when you need to.
>
> What you don't have always looks more appealing than what you do have.
>
> It is preferable to do a job even if it is delayed, than not do it at all.

■ Select the phrase from the box that best explains the meaning of each of the proverbs below. Write the correct phrase on the line.

1. First come, first served.

   _____

2. Good fences make good neighbors.

   _____

3. Honesty is the best policy.

   _____

4. It is no use crying over spilt milk.

   _____

ELD Standard
Demonstrate an understanding of figurative language and idiomatic expressions by responding to such expressions and using them appropriately.
ELA Standard
Identify idioms, analogies, metaphors, and similes in prose and poetry.

5. Many hands make light work.

_____

6. Never look a gift horse in the mouth.

_____

7. Necessity is the mother of invention.

_____

8. Better late than never.

_____

9. The early bird catches the worm.

_____

10. The grass is always greener on the other side of the fence.

_____

Name _____   Date _____

ⓐ Compound Words

▬▬ ▬▬ ▬▬ ▬▬ ▬▬ ▬▬ ▬▬ ▬▬ ▬▬ ▬▬ ▬▬ ▬▬ ▬▬ ▬▬ ▬▬

✔ Compound words are made by putting two words together.

   Example: hand + writing = handwriting

▬▬ ▬▬ ▬▬ ▬▬ ▬▬ ▬▬ ▬▬ ▬▬ ▬▬ ▬▬ ▬▬ ▬▬ ▬▬ ▬▬ ▬▬

▪ Write the two words making up each compound word, then use the compound words in complete sentences on the lines below.

1. bookkeeper = _____ + _____

   _____

2. townspeople = _____ + _____

   _____

3. childlike = _____ + _____

   _____

4. glassware = _____ + _____

   _____

5. ironworker = _____ + _____

   _____

6. backbreaking = _____ + _____

   _____

7. lifesaving = _____ + _____

   _____

8. lineup = _____ + _____

   _____

9. handwritten = _____ + _____

   _____

ELD Standard
   Use a standard dictionary to find the meaning of known vocabulary.
ELA Standard
   Identify and use compound words.

155

■ Look in the dictionary and find five more compound words. Write them on the lines below, and then write their definitions.

1. word: _____

_____

2. word: _____

_____

3. word: _____

_____

4. word: _____

_____

5. word: _____

_____

Name _____   Date _____

b Action Verbs

✔ Verbs are action words that describe what people do. Some verbs are specific to certain jobs or professions.

Example: *carpenter,* related action verbs ⟶ *to hammer, to saw, to drill*

■ Each circle contains the name of a different profession. Read the word, and then write three or four action verbs that are commonly associated with it. Follow the example.

Example:

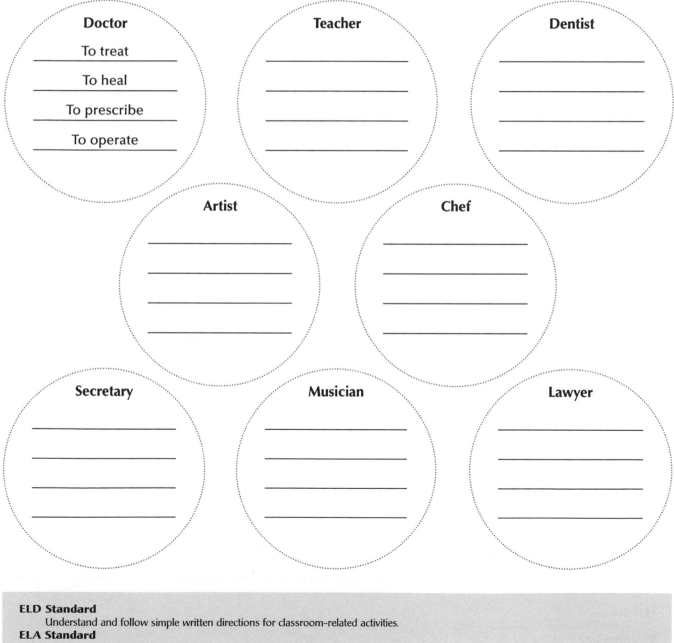

Doctor
To treat
To heal
To prescribe
To operate

Teacher

Dentist

Artist

Chef

Secretary

Musician

Lawyer

ELD Standard
  Understand and follow simple written directions for classroom-related activities.
ELA Standard
  Identify and use infinitives.

Name _____   Date _____

a Acronyms

━━ ━ ━ ━ ━ ━ ━ ━ ━ ━ ━ ━ ━ ━ ━ ━ ━ ━

✔ An acronym is a group of initials that stand for a word. Sometimes, these letters evolve into actual words.

Example: television = TV

━━ ━ ━ ━ ━ ━ ━ ━ ━ ━ ━ ━ ━ ━ ━ ━ ━ ━

■ Read each word below and write its acronym on the line.

1. digital video disc _____

2. compact disc _____

3. Federal Bureau of Investigation _____

4. Internal Revenue Service _____

5. as soon as possible _____

6. North Atlantic Treaty Organization _____

7. United States of America _____

8. European Union _____

9. self-contained underwater breathing apparatus _____

10. Organization of American States _____

11. Boy Scouts of America _____

12. United States Air Force _____

━━ ━ ━ ━ ━ ━ ━ ━ ━ ━ ━ ━ ━ ━ ━ ━ ━ ━

■ What do the following acronyms stand for? Use a dictionary or encyclopedia if you need help.

1. CIA _____

2. USN _____

3. NASA _____

4. PBS _____

5. USPS _____

6. UNESCO _____

ELD Standard
Collect information from various sources.
ELA Standard
Use correct capitalization.

Name   Date

b Prefixes

✔ Prefixes are letters that are placed at the beginning of a root word to change the meaning of the word.

✔ Sometimes adding a prefix can change the meaning of the word to its <u>opposite</u>.

■ Complete the following chart by providing the prefix, the root word, and the meaning of each of the following words.

Word	Prefix	Root Word	Meaning
nonsense			
nonfat			
nonsecure			
defrost			
decompose			
disorder			
dishonor			
nonfiction			
incurable			
indefinite			

■ Each box contains a prefix. Write as many words as you can think of that begin with each prefix.

tele-	*video-*	*micro-*

ELD Standard
    Apply knowledge of word relationships, such as roots and affixes.
ELA Standard
    Use knowledge of prefixes and suffixes to determine the meaning of words.

159

Name _____   Date _____

a Alphabetical Order

✔ When you put a list of words in alphabetical order, you need to look at the first letter of each word to see which one comes first. If two words begin with the same prefix, you need to look at the rest of the letters, in order to put them in correct alphabetical order.

■ Put each list of words in alphabetical order.

propose _____

progress _____

protect _____

pronounce _____

profess _____

produce _____

proclaim _____

biennial _____

bifocal _____

bicycle _____

bilingual _____

bilateral _____

biplane _____

bicultural _____

binocular _____

unripe _____

unlock _____

unknown _____

unpack _____

unpleasant _____

unroll _____

untidy _____

unfold _____

ELD Standard
Arrange words in alphabetical order.
ELA Standard
Demonstrate alphabet principle.

Name _____   Date _____

b Greek and Latin Roots

━━ ━━ ━━ ━━ ━━ ━━ ━━ ━━ ━━ ━━ ━━ ━━ ━━ ━━ ━━ ━━ ━━

✔ Many words in English have Greek and Latin roots.

━━ ━━ ━━ ━━ ━━ ━━ ━━ ━━ ━━ ━━ ━━ ━━ ━━ ━━ ━━ ━━ ━━

■ Can you think of words that have the following roots? Use a dictionary to look for words to put in each box.

anti-	*vid-/vis-*	*chrono-*	*auto-*

poly-	*-scope*	*geo-*

━━ ━━ ━━ ━━ ━━ ━━ ━━ ━━ ━━ ━━ ━━ ━━ ━━ ━━ ━━ ━━ ━━

■ What do these roots mean?

1. anti- _____

2. chrono- _____

3. poly- _____

4. vid-/vis- _____

5. auto- _____

6. scope- _____

7. geo- _____

ELD Standard
   Use a standard dictionary to determine the meaning of unknown words.
ELA Standard
   Use knowledge of Greek, Latin, and Anglo-Saxon roots and affixes to understand content-area vocabulary.

161

Name _____   Date _____

a Alphabetical Order

✔ Words are placed in alphabetical order according to their first letter. If words have the same first letter, then you must look at the second letter. If they have the same first and second letters, then continue comparing the letters until you find different letters and can place one before the other in alphabetical order.

rigging	schooner	submarine	purpose	nuclear
clipper	underwater	mast	steamship	research
military	heat	century	convert	energy

■ Arrange the words from the box in alphabetical order. Then use a dictionary to find the definition of each word.

1. word: _____

   definition: _____

2. word: _____

   definition: _____

3. word: _____

   definition: _____

4. word: _____

   definition: _____

5. word: _____

   definition: _____

6. word: _____

   definition: _____

7. word: _____

   definition: _____

ELD Standard
   Use a standard dictionary to determine the meaning of unknown words.
ELA Standard
   Demonstrate alphabet principle.

8. word: _____

   definition: _____

9. word: _____

   definition: _____

10. word: _____

    definition: _____

11. word: _____

    definition: _____

12. word: _____

    definition: _____

13. word: _____

    definition: _____

14. word: _____

    definition: _____

15. word: _____

    definition: _____

Name _____   Date _____

▣ Demonstrating Comprehension

■ Read the following paragraphs. Then answer the questions that follow, using complete sentences.

Nuclear Submarines

Submarines are vessels that operate underwater. They are very fast and some can even fire missiles while submerged. Almost all submarines are used by navies around the world, but a few are employed for scientific purposes.

In 1954, the first atomic-powered submarine was completed. It was called the *U.S. Nautilus*. Nuclear-powered submarines get their power from atomic reactors that produce heat to drive a turbine engine. These kinds of submarines can stay underwater for almost indefinite amounts of time. Some have even been around the globe without coming to the surface. The *U.S.S. Triton* was the first nuclear submarine to accomplish this.

1. How would you define a submarine?

   _____

2. What was the *U.S. Nautilus?*

   _____

3. What was one accomplishment of the *U.S.S. Triton?*

   _____

Prince Henry the Navigator

Prince Henry the navigator was born in 1364 in Oporto, Portugal. When he was in his twenties, he got the idea to explore the African coasts. He inherited a very large amount of money, and with it he built a castle in Sagres, where he dedicated himself to exploration. He launched voyages from Sagres and also gathered together astronomers and cartographers there. He built and observatory and founded the school of navigation in Europe, where he trained officers and crews destined to set out on voyages of exploration.

Prince Henry the Navigator contributed greatly to improvements in ship construction. Also in Sagres, the caravel, a small sailing ship, was invented.

ELD Standard
   Respond to comprehension questions about text by using detailed sentences.
ELA Standard
   Demonstrate appropriate English usage.

1. What country was Prince Henry the Navigator from?

   _____

2. How was Prince Henry able to build a castle in Sagres?

   _____

3. What did Prince Henry establish in Sagres?

   _____

4. What kind of ship was invented in Sagres?

   _____

Name _____   Date _____

c Writing an Essay

■ Select a topic from the box below, or another topic of your choice related to ships and boats. Use an encyclopedia or other references to look up information about the topic, and then write a paragraph summarizing what you learned. Be sure to use topic sentences and supporting details in your writing.

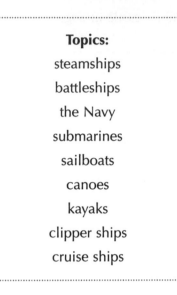

Topics:

steamships

battleships

the Navy

submarines

sailboats

canoes

kayaks

clipper ships

cruise ships

Title: _____

_____

_____

_____

_____

_____

_____

_____

_____

_____

_____

_____

ELD Standard
    Collect information from various sources and take notes on a given topic.
ELA Standard
    Use strategies of notetaking, outlining, and summarizing to impose structure on composition drafts.

Name _____   Date _____

a Negative Constructions in Writing

━━

✔ To show that something is not going to happen or is not possible, use the words *no* or *not*. This is called a *negative construction*.

✔ Negative constructions can be put into contractions using an apostrophe.

━━

■ Rewrite the following sentences, changing them into negative constructions.

1. There are planes in the air.

   _____

2. There are pilots in the cabin.

   _____

3. There are several jets in the hangar.

   _____

4. There is a reinforced door in the new plane.

   _____

5. There are supersonic jets flying across the Atlantic Ocean.

   _____

ELD Standard
   Edit and correct basic grammatical structures and usage of the conventions of writing.
ELA Standard
   Identify types and structure of sentences.

167

Name _____   Date _____

b Contractions

- How do you make the following negative constructions into contractions? Write the contractions on the lines provided.

1. could not _____

2. were not _____

3. is not _____

4. should not _____

5. would not _____

6. did not _____

7. can not _____

8. have not _____

9. will not _____

10. has not _____

- What do the following contractions stand for? Write the words on the lines provided.

1. I'd _____

2. they've _____

3. don't _____

4. you're _____

5. it'll _____

6. she's _____

7. it's _____

8. we'd _____

9. I'm _____

10. aren't _____

ELD Standard
Read and use contractions.
ELA Standard
Identify and correctly use contractions.

Name   Date

c Demonstrating Comprehension

■ Read the following essay about Alberto Santos-Dumont. Then answer the questions that follow.

Alberto Santos-Dumont

Alberto Santos-Dumont, a Brazilian who was born in 1873, was one of the great aviation pioneers. Although born in Brazil, he lived in Paris, France, from the age seventeen onward. He first built balloons and dirigible airships that ran on gasoline. His first successful flight was in an airship fueled by hydrogen. In 1901 Santos-Dumont flew around the Eiffel Tower—the first time anyone had done this. He won two prizes for this achievement.

In 1906, in a biplane made of bamboo and canvas, Santos-Dumont flew for 60 meters at a height of 2-3 meters. It was, he believed, the first successful airplane flight in a heavier-than-air powered flight, and he was recognized in the press around the world. Although the Wright Brothers from the United States were later acknowledged to have flown a heavier-than-air aircraft before Alberto Santos-Dumont, Santos-Dumont invented the device that enabled heavier-than-air planes to take off under their own power.

At one point, Alberto Santos-Dumont was concerned about having to use a pocket watch while flying, when he needed to keep both of his hands on the controls. He consulted his friend, Louis Cartier, who came up with a watch that could be worn on the wrist. Cartier invented the wristwatch for his friend, Alberto Santos-Dumont in 1904!

Santos-Dumont returned to Brazil in 1916. He had been diagnosed with multiple sclerosis six years earlier. After becoming seriously ill and very sad that airplanes were being used in wars, he took his own life in 1932.

1. Alberto Santos-Dumont moved to — when he was 17.
   - [ ] Brazil
   - [ ] South America
   - [ ] Paris
   - [ ] none of the above

2. Santos-Dumont invented the —
   - [ ] device that allowed planes to take off under their own power.
   - [ ] wristwatch.
   - [ ] heavier-than-air aircraft.
   - [ ] bamboo and canvas.

ELD Standard
Identify and explain the main ideas and critical details of informational materials, literary texts, and texts in content areas.
ELA Standard
Demonstrate comprehension by identifying answers in the text.

169

3. Santos-Dumont flew 60 meters in a — made of bamboo and canvas.

☐ balloon

☐ biplane

☐ dirigible

☐ helicopter

4. Alberto Santos-Dumont died in —

☐ 1916.

☐ 1906.

☐ 1873.

☐ 1932.

5. He became very ill from —

☐ influenza.

☐ cholera.

☐ plague.

☐ multiple sclerosis.

6. Alberto Santos-Dumont was a/an —

☐ Frenchman

☐ Argentine

☐ Brazilian

☐ American

Name   Date

a Common Abbreviations

━━ ━━ ━━ ━━ ━━ ━━ ━━ ━━ ━━ ━━ ━━ ━━ ━━ ━━ ━━ ━━ ━━

✔ Abbreviations, or shortened forms of words, are commonly used in measurements and other technical terms.

Examples: lb ⟶ pound

km ⟶ kilometer

━━ ━━ ━━ ━━ ━━ ━━ ━━ ━━ ━━ ━━ ━━ ━━ ━━ ━━ ━━ ━━ ━━

▪ Rewrite the following sentences and replace the underlined measurement term with its abbreviated form, as in the example.

Example:

The train traveled 200 <u>miles per hour</u>.

The train traveled at 200 mph.

1. The train hauled 22 <u>kilograms</u> of goods.

_____

2. My niece weighed 7 <u>pounds</u>, 11 ounces when she was born.

_____

3. My science teacher is named <u>Mister</u> Peterson.

_____

4. Whew! It's so hot—it must be at least 100 degrees <u>Fahrenheit</u>.

_____

5. Do you go to <u>Doctor</u> Hernandez in the downtown office?

_____

6. Sandra's grandmother came from the <u>United Kingdom</u>.

_____

7. We used to live on Oak <u>Street</u>, but now we live on Parkwood Court.

_____

ELD Standard
Recognize common abbreviations.
ELA Standard
Recognize common abbreviations.

171

8. She introduced me to <u>Colonel</u> Jaime Perez-Gomez.

_____

9. Last year Maria got a <u>Bachelor of Arts</u> degree in History from <u>University of California at Los Angeles</u>.

_____

10. The boy's feet grew two <u>inches</u> last year!

_____

■ Write the abbreviation for each word below.

Abbreviation

dozen   _____

centimeter   _____

Reverend   _____

William   _____

Celsius   _____

gallon   _____

hour   _____

Junior   _____

Name _____   Date _____

b Syllable Divisions

- Look up the following train-related words in the dictionary and write them on the lines provided in alphabetical order. Then classify words by their syllable divisions.

voltage	generation	signal	cylinder
semaphore	diesel	railroad	combustion
transport	electric	vehicle	boiler

1. _____   7. _____

2. _____   8. _____

3. _____   9. _____

4. _____   10. _____

5. _____   11. _____

6. _____   12. _____

Words with two syllables: _____

_____

_____

Words with three syllables: _____

_____

_____

Words with four syllables: _____

_____

_____

ELD Standard
Apply knowledge of basic syllabication rules when reading.
ELA Standard
Apply knowledge of basic syllabication rules when reading.

173

Name _____   Date _____

▣ Demonstrating Comprehension

▬▬ ▬ ▬ ▬ ▬▬ ▬ ▬▬ ▬ ▬▬ ▬▬ ▬ ▬▬ ▬ ▬▬ ▬ ▬

- Read the following passage about the first mass-produced automobiles. First, look up the underlined words in a dictionary and write down their definitions. Then, choose five of the words and use them in complete sentences.

When cars were first <u>built</u>, they were <u>assembled</u> by hand. This took a great deal of time and <u>required</u> highly-skilled people. As a result, <u>automobiles</u> were very <u>expensive</u> and not many people could afford them.

Henry Ford, a car <u>manufacturer</u> who lived in Detroit, <u>discovered</u> how to mass-produce cars by using standardized <u>parts</u>, and later, by using assembly lines. The first car <u>produced</u> with <u>standardized</u> parts came out in 1908. When the assembly line was <u>introduced</u> in 1914, the Model T was available in only one color. Henry Ford was <u>quoted</u> as saying that the Model T was <u>available</u> in "any color you like, so long as it's <u>black</u>." A car that once took several days to build now took only 12 hours. This resulted in cars becoming far less expensive and accessible to many more <u>people</u>.

Definitions:

1. _____

2. _____

3. _____

4. _____

5. _____

6. _____

7. _____

8. _____

9. _____

10. _____

11. _____

12. _____

ELD Standard
Produce independent writing with consistent use of capitalization and periods, and correct spelling.
ELA Standard
Clarify word meanings through the use of definitions, example, restatement, or contrast.

13. _____

14. _____

15. _____

Sentences:

1. _____

2. _____

3. _____

4. _____

5. _____

Name _____   Date _____

b Syllable Divisions/Writing an Essay

✔ Words with double consonants are usually divided between the consonants.

Example: **passage = pas-sage**

■ Read the following words divided into syllables and decide whether they are divided correctly. Mark the *correct* or *incorrect* box accordingly.

1. rud-der

   ❑ correct   ❑ incorrect

2. miss-peak

   ❑ correct   ❑ incorrect

3. as-sign

   ❑ correct   ❑ incorrect

4. e-ffort

   ❑ correct   ❑ incorrect

5. is-sue

   ❑ correct   ❑ incorrect

6. missi-on

   ❑ correct   ❑ incorrect

7. pas-sive

   ❑ correct   ❑ incorrect

8. de-ssert

   ❑ correct   ❑ incorrect

■ In the space below write a three-paragraph essay on some aspect of tools, technology, or any other topic you have learned about while doing the activities in this book.

Title: _____

_____
_____
_____
_____
_____
_____
_____

ELD Standard
   Proceed through the writing process to write short paragraphs that contain supporting details about a given topic.
ELA Standard
   Convey clear and accurate perspectives on the subject.

Name   Date

a Introductory Phrases in Sentences

✔ Sometimes a prepositional phrase is used as an introduction to a sentence in order to make it more interesting. Introductory phrases are separated from the rest of the sentence by a comma.

■ Rewrite each sentence so that it begins with an introductory (prepositional) phrase.

Example:

The glimmering sand dunes stretched for miles under the blue sky.

Under the blue sky, the glimmering sand dunes stretched for miles.

1. Marta and Pedro sang a duet in front of the huge audience.

2. Everyone rushes to buy hot cinnamon rolls between classes.

3. Kids can wear anything they want to wear outside of school.

4. The students have dances and fun events throughout the year.

5. Green ferns grow next to the giant redwood trees.

6. There used to be a very old house across the street.

7. We saw many beautiful paintings inside the museum.

8. The teacher provided delicious snacks after class.

ELD Standard
Use more complex vocabulary and sentences appropriate for language arts and other content areas.
ELA Standard
Combine short, related sentences with appositives, participal phrases, adjectives, adverbs and prepositional phrases.

9. People don't have enough to eat in many parts of the world.

_____

10. Congress passed the Clean Air Act in 1970.

_____

■ Use the introductory phrases in the box below to begin sentences. Write your complete sentences on the lines below.

Instead of	Aside from	On account of
According to	Because of	After the

1. _____

2. _____

3. _____

4. _____

5. _____

6. _____

Name _____   Date _____

b Demonstrating Comprehension/Compare and Contrast

■ Read the following passages. Then fill in the Venn diagram according to how the places described are alike and how they are different.

Lake Baikal

Lake Baikal is not only the deepest freshwater lake in the world, it is also the oldest. Lake Baikal is in the southern part of Siberia, near the Mongolian border. It holds 20% of the freshwater supply on Earth and has more species of plants and animals than any other lake in the world. Lake Baikal is nearly a mile (5,280 ft) deep. Lake Baikal is unbelievably clear. Many different kinds of mammals also live around Lake Baikal, including the world's only freshwater seal.

The Great Salt Lake

Located in the northern part of the state of Utah, in the United States, the Great Salt Lake is the largest saltwater lake in the Western Hemisphere. It is surrounded by sand and marshes. The average depth of the lake is 30 feet. The only lake in the world with higher salinity is the Dead Sea of Israel. The Great Salt Lake was once part of a much larger lake called Lake Bonneville, which spread across 20,000 square miles. No fish can survive in the salty waters of the Great Salt Lake. The only animals that can survive are brine shrimp, also called sea monkeys.

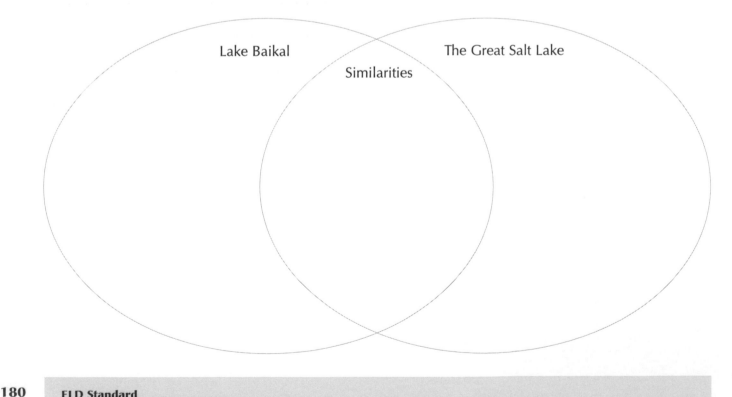

Lake Baikal   The Great Salt Lake

Similarities

ELD Standard
Understand and follow simple written directions for classroom-related activities.
ELA Standard
Compare and contrast information on the same topic after reading several passages or articles.

■ Answer the following questions by marking the correct answer with an **X**.

1. The Great Salt Lake —
   - ☐ is the deepest lake in the world.
   - ☐ was once part of a much larger lake.
   - ☐ lies near Mongolia.
   - ☐ is all of the above.
   - ☐ is none of the above.

2. Lake Baikal is —
   - ☐ the oldest freshwater lake in the world.
   - ☐ the home to the world's only freshwater seal.
   - ☐ in Siberia.
   - ☐ all of the above.
   - ☐ none of the above.

3. The Great Salt Lake —
   - ☐ is the most salty lake in the world.
   - ☐ is nearly a mile deep.
   - ☐ is on the Mongolian border.
   - ☐ is all of the above.
   - ☐ is none of the above.

4. Lake Baikal —
   - ☐ is the deepest freshwater lake in the world.
   - ☐ holds 20% of the Earth's saltwater supply.
   - ☐ has sea monkeys living in it.
   - ☐ is all of the above.
   - ☐ is none of the above.

■ Which lake is it? Using the clues, write the name of the lake that applies.

1. No fish can survive in it _____

2. Located in the northern part of Utah _____

3. Holds more species of plants and animals than any other lake _____

4. It is extremely clear _____

5. It is surrounded by sand and marshes _____

6. It was once a part of Lake Bonneville _____

Name   Date

a Transitive Verbs/Direct Object

✔ A transitive verb is a verb that requires a direct object. The direct object is usually a noun or a pronoun and it names the thing being acted upon by the verb.

✔ The direct object answers the questions *What?* or *Whom?*

■ Read the following sentences and answer the questions by marking the correct answer.

1. Five students forgot their books last Monday.
   What is the transitive verb in this sentence?
   ☐ students
   ☐ forgot
   ☐ their books
   ☐ Monday

2. I know people who speak French fluently!
   What is the direct object in this sentence?
   ☐ know
   ☐ French
   ☐ fluently
   ☐ people

3. My sister, Margaret, made a vase in her ceramics class.
   What is the transitive verb in this sentence?
   ☐ made
   ☐ Margaret
   ☐ a vase
   ☐ her

4. Do you see the snow on top of the mountains?
   What is the direct object in this sentence?
   ☐ mountains
   ☐ see
   ☐ the snow
   ☐ you

ELD Standard
   Identify and use parts of speech.
ELA Standard
   Identify all parts of speech.

Name _____   Date _____

b Passive Constructions

━━━━━━━━━━━━━━━━━━━━━━━━━━━━━━━━━━

✔ The passive voice is a weak voice, used to make statements of fact about topics when the acting agent is obvious or unimportant. It is also used to show that the subject is <u>acted upon</u>. It is important to not overuse the passive voice.

✔ The passive voice is formed by adding the past participle of a verb to the appropriate form of the verb *to be*.

Examples: The California mountain lion <u>is endangered</u>.

The California condor <u>is recovering</u> from near-extinction.

━━━━━━━━━━━━━━━━━━━━━━━━━━━━━━━━━━

▪ Look at each of the words below and write a sentence using the passive voice for each.

1. Florida crocodile

_____

2. Manatee

_____

3. Florida mangrove swamp

_____

4. Florida panther

_____

5. Heron

_____

ELD Standard
Produce independent writing with consistent use of capitalization, punctuation, and correct spelling.
ELA Standard
Identify all parts of speech.

183

Name _____   Date _____

c Writing an Essay

■ Select a topic from the box below. Research the topic using encyclopedias, reference books, or Internet search engines. Take notes and create an outline. Then, write a three-paragraph essay in the space provided.

Topics

Elephants	Florida cougar	Black rhinoceros	Whooping crane
Blue whale	Snow leopard	Giant armadillo	Tiger
Gorilla	Giant panda	California condor	Seahorse

Title: _____

_____

_____

_____

_____

_____

_____

_____

_____

_____

_____

_____

_____

_____

_____

_____

_____

_____

_____

ELD Standard
Proceed through the writing process to write short paragraphs that contain support details about a given topic.
ELA Standard
Identify topics; ask and evaluate questions; and develop ideas leading to inquiry, investigation, and research.

Name _____   Date _____

a Independent and Dependent Clauses

✔ Complex sentences are made up of two clauses.

✔ A clause is a group of words containing a subject and a predicate.

✔ Independent clauses are grammatically complete and can stand alone as sentences.

✔ Dependent clauses (subordinate clauses) cannot stand alone, and by themselves are sentence fragments.

■ Read the sentences below. Look at the underlined group of words and decide whether it is an independent or a dependent clause. Write *Independent Clause* or *Dependent Clause* on the line.

1. After the lake freezes, <u>the plants die</u>.

   _____

2. <u>The plane flew very low</u>, and the people waved from the ground.

   _____

3. You won't be able to play on the team <u>if you get bad grades</u>.

   _____

4. <u>Since you'll be earning your own money from your job</u>, you can buy your own CDs.

   _____

5. Since Rogelio worked hard campaigning in the election, <u>he was delighted to find out that he had won</u>.

   _____

6. <u>When you see the light turn yellow</u>, you should always stop your car!

   _____

■ Underline the dependent clause in each of the following sentences.

1. If you study geology, you learn about the causes of earthquakes.

2. I called my husband to come look when I spotted the iceberg.

ELD Standard
   Identify basic vocabulary, mechanics, and sentence structures in a piece of writing.
ELA Standard
   Identify and correctly use independent and dependent clauses.

3. When it reaches a certain temperature it is no longer safe to be outdoors.

4. Judging from her reaction, I could tell the storm had had a big impact on her family.

5. In order to survive, you must be very well prepared.

6. Although it's extremely cold there, the professor still goes to Antarctica each year.

Name   Date

b Subordinate Conjunctions

✔ Subordinate conjunctions introduce dependent clauses in complex sentences.

after	as	as long as	before	in order that
so that	though	until	where	while
although	as if	as though	if	since
that	unless	when	whereas	so that

■ Write ten complete sentences using subordinate conjunctions from the above box. Circle or highlight the subordinate conjunction in each sentence.

Example:

I went to my piano lesson (after) I made lunch.

Roberto saved his money (so that) he could buy a video game.

1. _____

2. _____

3. _____

4. _____

5. _____

6. _____

7. _____

8. _____

9. _____

10. _____

ELD Standard
Recognize the function of connectors in written text.
ELA Standard
Use conjunctions to connect ideas.

Name   Date

a Antonyms/Synonyms

✔ Antonyms are words that have opposite meanings.

✔ Synonyms are words that have the same meaning.

■ Write the antonym of the following words.

Word	Antonym
dry	
shrink	
highest	
hot	
up	
near	
beautiful	

■ Choose the answer that is the antonym of each word.

1. daughter
   - [ ] sister
   - [ ] brother
   - [ ] son
   - [ ] mother

2. always
   - [ ] never
   - [ ] sometimes
   - [ ] often
   - [ ] commonly

3. awake
   - [ ] alert
   - [ ] inattentive
   - [ ] wide-eyed
   - [ ] asleep

4. city
   - [ ] county
   - [ ] countryside
   - [ ] nation
   - [ ] town

5. foolish
   - [ ] silly
   - [ ] dumb
   - [ ] silent
   - [ ] clever

6. empty
   - [ ] full
   - [ ] vacant
   - [ ] dull
   - [ ] closed

ELD Standard
Recognize simple antonyms and synonyms in written text. Expand recognition of them and begin to use appropriately.

ELA Standard
Understand and explain common antonyms and synonyms.

■ Read each pair of words and decide whether they are antonyms or synonyms. Mark the correct answers in the appropriate column.

	Synonyms	Antonyms
1. easy / difficult	❏	❏
2. fabulous / terrific	❏	❏
3. lock / unlock	❏	❏
4. often / seldom	❏	❏
5. crease / fold	❏	❏
6. simple / complex	❏	❏
7. grow / increase	❏	❏
8. dull / sharp	❏	❏
9. original / copy	❏	❏
10. forgive / pardon	❏	❏
11. hollow / solid	❏	❏
12. miniature / gigantic	❏	❏
13. even / level	❏	❏
14. custom / habit	❏	❏
15. knowledge / ignorance	❏	❏

Name _____   Date _____

b Relative Pronouns in Complex Sentences

━ ━

✔ Complex sentences are made up of an independent clause and a dependent clause. Subordinate conjunctions can join the two parts of a complex sentence.

✔ Relative pronouns can also connect two parts of a complex sentence. Some relative pronouns are *that, who, whose, which, what, who, whoever, whatever,* and *whichever.*

  Example: Death Valley has many kinds of cactus that bloom in beautiful colors.

    Independent clause: Death Valley has many kinds of cactus

    Dependent clause: that bloom in beautiful colors

━ ━

■ Answer each question by providing the correct information.

1. The rainfall in Death Valley is very low, which makes it impossible for many animals to survive there.

   What is the independent clause? _____

   What is the dependent clause? _____

   What is the relative pronoun? _____

2. The class traveled to the desert where they studied the local flora.

   What is the independent clause? _____

   What is the dependent clause? _____

   What is the relative pronoun? _____

3. Cougars and foxes thrive in the desert environment, whatever the weather or temperature.

   What is the independent clause? _____

   What is the dependent clause? _____

   What is the relative pronoun? _____

ELD Standard
  Use more complex vocabulary and sentences appropriate for language arts and other content areas.
ELA Standard
  Identify and correctly use pronouns.

4. I plan to write a report on the Joshua Tree, the mesquite tree, or the holly tree, whichever one I see first.

What is the independent clause? _____

What is the dependent clause? _____

What is the relative pronoun? _____

■ Write three complex sentences about Death Valley. Underline the relative pronoun in each one.

1. _____

2. _____

3. _____

Name _____   Date _____

a Adjectives

━━ ━━ ━ ━━ ━ ━ ━ ━━ ━ ━ ━━ ━ ━━ ━ ━━ ━━ ━ ━━ ━ ━ ━━

✔ Adjectives are words that describe nouns. They tell what things look, feel, and sound like. Adjectives are generally placed before the noun.

━━ ━━ ━ ━━ ━ ━ ━ ━━ ━ ━ ━━ ━ ━━ ━ ━━ ━━ ━ ━━ ━ ━ ━━

■ Complete the following adjective-noun pairs by filling in the blank spaces with an adjective or a noun.

1. beautiful _____   5. colorful _____

2. _____ fish   6. _____ eaglet

3. _____ snake   7. furry _____

4. majestic _____   8. powerful _____

━━ ━━ ━ ━━ ━ ━ ━ ━━ ━ ━ ━━ ━ ━━ ━ ━━ ━━ ━ ━━ ━ ━ ━━

■ Complete the word webs below by writing four adjectives that describe each endangered animal. You may want to consult an encyclopedia or research the Internet. Write the adjectives on the lines provided.

humpback whale

grizzly bear

California condor

ELD Standard
Collect information from various sources.
ELA Standard
Place modifiers correctly.

Name _____   Date _____

b Writing an Essay on a Given Topic

▬▬ ▬ ▬ ▬ ▬ ▬ ▬ ▬ ▬ ▬ ▬ ▬ ▬ ▬ ▬ ▬ ▬ ▬

✔ North American raptors (also called *birds of prey*) include the eagles, falcons, hawks, owls and vultures.

▬▬ ▬ ▬ ▬ ▬ ▬ ▬ ▬ ▬ ▬ ▬ ▬ ▬ ▬ ▬ ▬ ▬ ▬

■ Select one of the birds in the box. Write an essay after researching your topic in the library and/or online.

Northern goshawk	Harris's hawk
spotted owl	snail kite
osprey	American peregrine falcon
ferruginous pygmy owl	

Title: _____

_____

_____

_____

_____

_____

_____

_____

_____

_____

_____

_____

_____

_____

_____

_____

_____

_____

ELD Standard
Collect information on various sources and take notes on a given topic.
ELA Standard
Include evidence compiled through the formal research process.

Name _____   Date _____

a Capitalization of Proper Nouns

▬ ▬ ▬ ▬ ▬ ▬ ▬ ▬ ▬ ▬ ▬ ▬ ▬ ▬ ▬ ▬ ▬ ▬

✔ Some animals and plants bear the name of a country, a state, or a region. The only word in these names that is capitalized is the name of the place (proper noun), not the animal or plant (common noun.)

▬ ▬ ▬ ▬ ▬ ▬ ▬ ▬ ▬ ▬ ▬ ▬ ▬ ▬ ▬ ▬ ▬ ▬

■ Rewrite the following names of animals and plants, remembering to capitalize the names of countries, states, or regions.

african elephant	california clapper rail	napa bluegrass
alabama sturgeon	houston toad	chinese paddlefish
texas ocelot	mauritius kestrel	california jewelflower
santa cruz long-toed salamander	oregon silverspot butterfly	shasta crayfish
iberian lynx	american alligator	fresno kangaroo rat
san diego fairy shrimp	monterey spineflower	hudson bay polar bear
santa rosa island manzanita	bear valley sandwort	
asian elephant	hawaiian crow	

1. _____   12. _____

2. _____   13. _____

3. _____   14. _____

4. _____   15. _____

5. _____   16. _____

6. _____   17. _____

7. _____   18. _____

8. _____   19. _____

9. _____   20. _____

10. _____   21. _____

11. _____   22. _____

ELD Standard
Edit writing for basic conventions.
ELA Standard
Use correct capitalization.

Name _____   Date _____

b Synonyms

▬ ▬

✔ Synonyms are words that have the same meaning.

✔ A thesaurus is a reference book that provides you with synonyms for many words.

▬ ▬

■ Using a thesaurus, rewrite each sentence, replacing the underlined word with an appropriate synonym.

1. The <u>beautiful</u> bird flew to its nest.

   _____

2. Every tiger has a <u>different</u> pattern of stripes.

   _____

3. The tiger <u>grabbed</u> the gazelle by the neck.

   _____

4. The climates in different African ecosystems <u>vary</u> widely.

   _____

5. The big cats move <u>silently</u> through the jungle.

   _____

6. We watched the monkeys <u>leap</u> from tree to tree in search of food.

   _____

ELD Standard
Recognize simple antonyms and synonyms in written text. Expand recognition of them and begin to use appropriately.
ELA Standard
Use a thesaurus to determine related words and concepts.

195

■ Read each pair of words, and then decide whether the second word is a good synonym for the first word. Check *yes* or *no* for each pair.

	Yes	No
1. wild / **unruly**	❑	❑
2. playful / **shy**	❑	❑
3. crafty / **cunning**	❑	❑
4. intimidate / **threaten**	❑	❑
5. keep / **donate**	❑	❑
6. guts / **insides**	❑	❑
7. fatigue / **vigor**	❑	❑
8. call / **yell**	❑	❑
9. band / **stripe**	❑	❑
10. bank / **mountaintop**	❑	❑
11. ample / **insufficient**	❑	❑
12. goodness / **virtue**	❑	❑

Name _____   Date _____

a Adjectives Used as Comparatives

▬ ▬ ▬ ▬ ▬ ▬ ▬ ▬ ▬ ▬ ▬ ▬ ▬ ▬ ▬ ▬ ▬ ▬ ▬

✔ You form the comparative form of an adjective by adding -er to the simple form of the adjective. Often, you put the word *more* in front of the adjective, particularly when the word has more than two syllables.

▬ ▬ ▬ ▬ ▬ ▬ ▬ ▬ ▬ ▬ ▬ ▬ ▬ ▬ ▬ ▬ ▬ ▬ ▬

■ Choose ten adjectives from the box below and use them in comparative sentences.

Examples: Adjectives: friendly, damaged

          The pet cat was <u>friendlier</u> than the feral cat.

          The field was <u>more damaged</u> than the nearby park.

strange	pretty	precious	tall
nutritious	horrible	ordinary	magnificent
wasteful	striped	tame	gigantic
wonderful	handsome	gorgeous	beautiful

1. _____

2. _____

3. _____

4. _____

5. _____

6. _____

7. _____

8. _____

9. _____

10. _____

ELD Standard
    Use more complex vocabulary and sentences appropriate for language arts and other content areas.
ELA Standard
    Identify types and structure of sentences.

197

Name _____   Date _____

b Compound Sentences

━━ ━ ━ ━ ━ ━ ━ ━ ━ ━ ━ ━ ━ ━ ━ ━ ━ ━ ━ ━

✓ A compound sentence combines two (or more) related independent clauses with a coordinating conjunction. The coordinating conjunctions are *but, and, or, for, nor, yet* and *so*. The clauses are usually separated by a comma.

━━ ━ ━ ━ ━ ━ ━ ━ ━ ━ ━ ━ ━ ━ ━ ━ ━ ━ ━ ━

▪ Read each pair of sentences below. Rewrite them as a compound sentence, using an appropriate coordinating conjunction, and adding any necessary auxiliary words, such as pronouns.

1. Crocodiles have narrow snouts.
   Alligators have broad snouts.

   _____

2. Alligators can walk along slowly dragging their tails.
   Alligators can walk on their toes with their tails up in the air.

   _____

   _____

3. Alligators are a blackish color.
   Crocodiles are an olive brown color.

   _____

4. Alligators eat insects, crabs, frogs, turtles, and other things.
   They also eat dead animals.

   _____

   _____

5. Crocodiles lay their eggs in saltwater.
   Alligators lay their eggs in freshwater.

   _____

6. Alligators live in rivers.
   Alligators live in swamps and freshwater lakes.

   _____

   _____

ELD Standard
Use more complex vocabulary and sentences appropriate for language arts and other content areas.
ELA Standard
Identify and use coordinating conjunctions in writing and speaking.

7. Alligators are carnivores.

   Alligators sometimes eat vegetation.

   _____

8. The number of alligators has increased greatly as a result of protection.

   The alligator is not considered an endangered species.

   _____

   _____

9. Alligators swim very well.

   Alligators have webbed feet.

   _____

Name _____   Date _____

a Compound Words

✔ Some words in English are made from putting two words together. These words are called compound words.

Example: ever + green = evergreen

■ Draw a line from a word in the left column to a word in the right column, making a compound word. Then write the word on the line to the right.

grape	pond	_____
moon	top	_____
fish	bug	_____
mountain	stool	_____
pine	light	_____
night	flake	_____
lady	berry	_____
toad	hopper	_____
thunder	vine	_____
sun	time	_____
water	pool	_____
snow	cone	_____
whirl	light	_____
blue	stream	_____
down	fall	_____
grass	storm	_____

ELD Standard
   Read compound words.
ELA Standard
   Identify and use compound words.

Illustrate nine of the compound words. Write each word in its box.

Word:	Word:	Word:

Word:	Word:	Word:

Word:	Word:	Word:

Name _____   Date _____

b Relative Pronouns

━━

✔ A relative pronoun is a pronoun that replaces a noun and also links the dependent clause (where the relative pronoun is) to the main clause.

✔ The most common relative pronouns are *that*, *what*, *who*, *whom*, and *which*.

━━

▪ Use each of the words below in a complete sentence with a dependent clause linked to the main clause with the word *that*, as in the example. Underline the dependent clause and circle the relative pronoun in each sentence.

Example:

moose

In Yellowstone we glimpsed a moose (*that*) was drinking in a stream.

1. volcano

_____

2. minerals

_____

3. geyser

_____

4. geothermal

_____

5. waterfall

_____

6. steam

_____

7. hot spring

_____

ELD Standard
Identify and use parts of speech.
ELA Standard
Identify and correctly use pronouns.

8. evergreens

_____

9. bison

_____

10. salamanders

_____

Name _____   Date _____

a Types of Sentences/Asking and Answering Questions

✓ There are three types of sentences: declarative, interrogative, and exclamatory. Interrogative sentences ask questions and end with question marks. They start with a question word (*who, what, where, when, why* and *how*) and may use the helping verb *(to) do.*

■ Look at the words below and write questions about each one. Use the word *do* following each question word. Then answer the question with a complete sentence.

Example:

Q: Why <u>do</u> jellyfish have tentacles?

A: Jellyfish have tentacles so they can capture prey. _____

| sea stars | shark | lobster | sea otter | migrate | sunfish |
| seahorse | whale | tuna | fish tank | tide pool | |

1. **Q:** _____

   A: _____

2. **Q:** _____

   A: _____

3. **Q:** _____

   A: _____

4. **Q:** _____

   A: _____

5. **Q:** _____

   A: _____

6. **Q:** _____

   A: _____

ELD Standard
   Edit writing for basic conventions.
ELA Standard
   Identify types and structure of sentences.

7. **Q:** _____

   A: _____

8. **Q:** _____

   A: _____

9. **Q:** _____

   A: _____

10. **Q:** _____

    A: _____

11. **Q:** _____

    A: _____

Name _____   Date _____

b Vocabulary/Using a Dictionary

■ Look up the following vocabulary words in a dictionary. Write the words in alphabetical order. Then write the definitions on the lines provided.

kelp	forest	aquarium	protect	sunfish	public	shore
whale	tide pool	migration	ocean	exhibit	shark	crab

1. _____

_____

2. _____

_____

3. _____

_____

4. _____

_____

5. _____

_____

6. _____

_____

7. _____

_____

8. _____

_____

9. _____

_____

ELD Standard
Use a standard dictionary to determine meaning of unknown words.
ELA Standard
Use a dictionary to learn the meaning and other features of unknown words.

10. _____

_____

11. _____

_____

12. _____

_____

13. _____

_____

14. _____

_____

Name _____   Date _____

ⓐ Collective Nouns/Writing an Essay

▬ ▬

■ Read the following expressions and fill in the word or words that are missing. Use a dictionary to help you.

1. A venom of _____   4. A colony of _____

2. A swarm of _____   5. A school of _____

3. A team of _____   6. A herd of _____

▬ ▬

■ Write a three-paragraph essay choosing one of the following topics. You may want to consult an encyclopedia or research the topics on the Internet.

Ecosystems	National Parks	Endangered animals

_____

_____

_____

_____

_____

_____

_____

_____

_____

_____

_____

_____

_____

_____

ELD Standard
Collect information from various sources.
ELA Standard
Use a dictionary to learn the meaning and other features of unknown words.

Name _____   Date _____

b Demonstrating Comprehension

━━ ━━ ━━ ━━ ━━ ━━ ━━ ━━ ━━ ━━ ━━ ━━ ━━ ━━ ━━ ━━ ━━

- Read the following essay about the San Diego Wild Animal Park. Then answer the questions that follow using complete sentences.

The San Diego Wild Animal Park

On May 10, 1972, the San Diego Wild Animal Park opened. It was designed to give animals a lot of room to roam and people the opportunity to see animals as they might be viewed in their native habitats. Visitors to the park travel around as if on safari on the *Wgasa Bush Line Railway*, a tram ride that passes through the rolling hills, cliffs, and plains of the park. People can ride this train around the large park for an hour and see hundreds of different kinds of African and Asian animals roaming, grazing, resting, running, and mingling as they do in the wild.

At the San Diego Wild Animal Park there are 38 endangered species of mammals and 11 endangered species of birds. Hundreds of babies have been born at the San Diego Wild Animal Park—babies of endangered species and some nearly-extinct species. Some have even been re-introduced back into the wild. There are more than 3,500 exotic animals at the park.

1. Why was the San Diego Wild Animal Park designed in the way it was, with wide-open spaces?

_____

2. When did the park officially open?

_____

3. How many animals live at the San Diego Wild Animal Park?

_____

4. How do people get around the park to see the animals?

_____

5. What kinds of terrain do they have at the San Diego Wild Animal Park?

_____

6. How many species of endangered birds live at the San Diego Wild Animal Park?

_____

ELD Standard
Identify and explain the main ideas and critical details of informational materials, literary texts, and texts in content areas.
ELA Standard
Demonstrate comprehension by identifying answers in the text.

7. What animals have been re-introduced back into the wild?

_____

8. What is the tram at the San Diego Wild Animal Park called?

_____

9. What kinds of things can you see animals doing at the park?

_____

Name _____   Date _____

ⓐ Passive Constructions

▬ ▬ ▬ ▬ ▬ ▬ ▬ ▬ ▬ ▬ ▬ ▬ ▬ ▬ ▬ ▬ ▬ ▬ ▬

✔ A passive construction is formed with a form of the verb *to be* and the past participle of the main verb.

▬ ▬ ▬ ▬ ▬ ▬ ▬ ▬ ▬ ▬ ▬ ▬ ▬ ▬ ▬ ▬ ▬ ▬ ▬

■ Change the following sentences to the indicated tense, as in the example. You may need to change the word order.

Example:

Put into the present passive

Dozens of students buy notebooks and books from Mr. Garcia.

Notebooks and books are bought by dozens of students from Mr. Garcia.
_____

Put into the past passive

1. The archaeologists found many fossils and remnants of the ancient culture.

_____

2. It took many years to complete the Great Wall of China.

_____

3. The workmen completed the wall in 1644.

_____

Put into the present passive

1. Many people photograph the wall every day.

_____

2. The Chinese built walls on their borders as early as 600 B.C.

_____

Put into the present perfect progressive

1. For centuries, people have done studies on the Great Wall.

_____

2. People orbiting the Earth in spaceships have seen the Great Wall.

_____

ELD Standard
    Use complete sentences and correct word order.
ELA Standard
    Identify and use participles.

Put into the present progressive passive

1. Every season they bring large groups of tourists to China.

   _____

2. Craftsmen repair the wall constantly.

   _____

Name _____   Date _____

b Modal Verbs

━━ ━━ ━━ ━━ ━━ ━━ ━━ ━━ ━━ ━━ ━━ ━━ ━━ ━━ ━━ ━━

✔ Modal verbs are put in sentences to help the main verb express meaning.

✔ The modals *have*, *ought*, and *need* are followed by the infinitive of the verb. Most others are followed by the simple form of the verb.

━━ ━━ ━━ ━━ ━━ ━━ ━━ ━━ ━━ ━━ ━━ ━━ ━━ ━━ ━━ ━━

▪ Complete the sentences below by filling in modal verbs.

Example:

Before you travel to Asia, you (need)

need to get vaccinations. _____

1. If you are going to do a lot of walking, you (should)

   _____

2. In order to learn to speak Chinese, you (need)

   _____

3. If you need assistance while you are out of the country, you (should)

   _____

4. To take a long trip you (have)

   _____

5. If you want to have the right currency, you (need)

   _____

ELD Standard
    Use correct parts of speech.
ELA Standard
    Identify and use infinitives.

213

Complete the following statements by adding a verb, and using words from the box.

tower	structure	road	passport
wall	construction	ancient	history

1. I have to _____.

2. I ought to _____.

3. You may _____.

4. She must _____.

5. Mr. Smith has _____.

6. You will _____.

7. He needs _____.

8. We must _____.

Unit 9   Lesson 7.82

Name   Date

a Capitalization of Proper Nouns

✔ Names of historical landmarks, buildings, monuments, and other structures are proper nouns and begin with capital letters.

■ In a box below is a list of nouns. Write all the proper nouns in the chart that follows under the correct heading. Be sure to spell them with capital letters.

the white house	the liberty bell	u.s. capitol
tower of london	mount rushmore	temple of neptune
arlington national cemetery	the alamo	the colosseum

Buildings	Monuments / Landmarks

ELD Standard
    Edit writing for basic conventions.
ELA Standard
    Use correct capitalization.

215

■ Using an encyclopedia, look for the names of other monuments and landmarks. Draw four of them, labeling each drawing with the name of the chosen monument or landmark.

Name: _____

Name: _____

Name: _____

Name: _____

Name _____   Date _____

ⓑ Order of Adjectives in a Sentence

▬▬ ▬▬ ▬▬ ▬▬ ▬▬ ▬▬ ▬▬ ▬▬ ▬▬ ▬▬ ▬▬ ▬▬ ▬▬ ▬▬ ▬▬

✔ When two or more adjectives are listed in a sentence, they should be placed in the following order.

> 1. number   :   5. shape
> 2. size   :   6. color
> 3. quality   :   7. material
> 4. age   :   8. origin

■ In each box there are several adjectives and a noun. Put them in the correct sequence in an original complete sentence.

Example:

Adjectives: tall, four, wooden
Noun: buildings

_____The four tall wooden buildings were badly damaged after the fire._____

Adjectives: small, Japanese, metal, square
Noun: lamp

_____

Adjectives: French, red, wooden, expensive
Noun: torch

_____

ELD Standard
    Use common verbs, nouns, and high-frequency modifiers in writing simple sentences.
ELA Standard
    Place modifiers properly.

217

Adjectives: stone, tall, ancient, one, brown
Noun: watchtower

_____

Adjectives: silver, fancy, European, old
Noun: car

_____

Adjectives: enormous, long, two, new, gray
Noun: ships

_____

Name _____   Date _____

a Gerunds

✔ When the *-ing* form of a verb is used as a noun, it is called a gerund. It can be the subject of a sentence. Often, this construction is used when talking about sports or hobbies.

Example: **Surfing has been a popular sport for many decades.**

■ Look at the words in the box and write a sentence about each one on the lines that follow. The sentence should give information about the hobby or sport.

skiing	running	skydiving	singing
horseback riding	painting	swimming	dancing

1. _____

2. _____

3. _____

4. _____

5. _____

6. _____

7. _____

8. _____

■ Think of other gerunds used as nouns that refer to hobbies or sports. Write them in the box below.

GERUNDS

_____ _____ _____

_____ _____ _____

_____ _____ _____

_____ _____ _____

ELD Standard
    Write an increasing number of words and simple sentences appropriate for language arts and other content areas.
ELA Standard
    Identify all parts of speech.

Name _____   Date _____

b Order of Adjectives in a Sentence

✔ When a series of adjectives appear in a sentence, they should be placed in a particular order. Review the box below, which shows the correct order.

1. number	5. shape
2. size	6. color
3. quality	7. material
4. age	8. origin

■ Write complete sentences using series of adjectives, following the order shown above.

1. _____

2. _____

3. _____

4. _____

5. _____

■ Think of four adjectives that describe each of the following nouns. Write them in the proper order on the lines provided.

1. life vest _____

2. scenery _____

3. river _____

4. paddle _____

5. gear _____

ELD Standard
   Write an increasing number of words and simple sentences appropriate for language arts and other content areas.
ELA Standard
   Place modifiers properly.

Name _____   Date _____

◧ *May* and *Might*

✔ You use the terms *may* and *might* to express possibility.

✔ The modal *may* can also be used to ask for and give permission.

■ Rewrite the sentences below, using the words *may* or *might* to express possibility or uncertainty.

Example:

  Donna will move to Boston. (might)

  Donna might move to Boston. _____

1. I will go to Alaska when I am eighteen. (might)

   _____

2. Dr. Sanchez will speak to a conference about children's health. (may)

   _____

3. Will you go to summer school to take Spanish next summer? (might)

   _____

4. My family will celebrate Cinco de Mayo by going out to our favorite restaurant. (might)

   _____

5. Our band will be in the performance at the Opera House in December. (may)

   _____

6. Lila's mother will bring a sweet potato pie to the meeting. (may)

   _____

7. How will you prepare dessert for the party tomorrow night? (might)

   _____

8. Pamela will play her drum in the school talent show. (might)

   _____

ELD Standard
Write an increasing number of words and simple sentences appropriate for language arts and other content areas.
ELA Standard
Demonstrate appropriate English usage.

221

■ Formulate questions or sentences that match the descriptions below, as in the example. Underline the modal in each question.

Example:

A boy wants permission to go to the library to use an encyclopedia

<u>May</u> I go to the library to use an encyclopedia? _____

1. The mother gives permission for her son to go to the Computer Club after school.

    _____

2. The principal gives permission for a student to go to the front of the lunch line.

    _____

3. A teacher gives a student permission to write an answer on the board.

    _____

4. Two students ask permission to use the telephone in the school office.

    _____

Name _____   Date _____

b *If* Statements

▬ ▬ ▬ ▬ ▬ ▬ ▬ ▬ ▬ ▬ ▬ ▬ ▬ ▬ ▬ ▬ ▬ ▬ ▬ ▬

✔ *If* statements are used when you are talking about things that will or might happen, if another thing happens first.

Example: *If* I put on my swimsuit, *then* I can go in the pool.

▬ ▬ ▬ ▬ ▬ ▬ ▬ ▬ ▬ ▬ ▬ ▬ ▬ ▬ ▬ ▬ ▬ ▬ ▬ ▬

▪ Write an *if* statement that completes the sentence that follows the blank.

1. _____,
   then I can make a dessert with coconut and papaya.

2. _____,
   then we will have good entertainment at the luau.

3. _____,
   then she will serve the sweet potato pie to the guests.

4. _____,
   then you can drink the fresh pineapple juice.

▬ ▬ ▬ ▬ ▬ ▬ ▬ ▬ ▬ ▬ ▬ ▬ ▬ ▬ ▬ ▬ ▬ ▬ ▬ ▬

▪ Complete the sentences below by providing a *then* statement.

1. If I get to go to Hawaii during summer vacation,

   _____.

2. If the hula dancers are free on the 16th of June,

   _____.

3. If you rent a snorkel and fins from the dive shop,

   _____.

4. If you put a lot of sunscreen on before you go out in the sun,

   _____.

ELD Standard
   Use more complex vocabulary and sentences appropriate for language arts and other content areas.
ELA Standard
   Identify types and structure of sentences.

Name _____   Date _____

ⓐ Superlatives

▬▬ ▬▬ ▬▬ ▬▬ ▬▬ ▬▬ ▬▬ ▬▬ ▬▬ ▬▬ ▬▬ ▬▬ ▬▬ ▬▬ ▬▬ ▬▬ ▬▬ ▬▬ ▬▬ ▬▬

✔ The superlative is used to compare more than two people or things. To form the superlative, you need to use the definite article *the*, with the suffix *-est* added to the end of most adjectives. Superlatives are also used to talk about world records.

▬▬ ▬▬ ▬▬ ▬▬ ▬▬ ▬▬ ▬▬ ▬▬ ▬▬ ▬▬ ▬▬ ▬▬ ▬▬ ▬▬ ▬▬ ▬▬ ▬▬ ▬▬ ▬▬ ▬▬

■ Use a search engine on the Internet, such as *Ask Jeeves* (www.ask.com) to look up information on the following topics. Then formulate superlative sentences, as in the example. Highlight or underline the superlative in each sentence.

Facts:

Example:

   fast fish

_____ The cosmopolitan sailfish is <u>the fastest</u> fish in the sea. _____

1. tall building

   _____

2. long river

   _____

3. cold place on Earth

   _____

4. expensive piece of art

   _____

5. old person

   _____

6. dry place on Earth

   _____

7. fast bird

   _____

ELD Standard
   Use more complex vocabulary and sentences appropriate for language arts and other content areas.
ELA Standard
   Demonstrate appropriate English usage.

8. fast animal on land

_____

Opinions:

Example:

   good artist

               <u>The best</u> artist in the world was Claude Monet.
_____

1. beautiful music

_____

2. good athlete

_____

3. computer game

_____

4. good place to go on vacation

_____

5. good hobby

_____

6. good holiday

_____

Name _____   Date _____

b Modals that Express Possibility

▬▬ ▬▬ ▬▬ ▬▬ ▬▬ ▬▬ ▬▬ ▬▬ ▬▬ ▬▬ ▬▬ ▬▬ ▬▬ ▬▬ ▬▬ ▬▬ ▬▬ ▬▬

✔ The words *maybe* and *perhaps* are modals that express possibility. Other modals that express possibility are *may* and *might*.

▬▬ ▬▬ ▬▬ ▬▬ ▬▬ ▬▬ ▬▬ ▬▬ ▬▬ ▬▬ ▬▬ ▬▬ ▬▬ ▬▬ ▬▬ ▬▬ ▬▬ ▬▬

■ Answer the questions with complete sentences, using one of the four modals in the box to express possibility or uncertainty.

maybe	perhaps	may	might

1. Why do skydivers jump out of airplanes with parachutes?

   _____

2. Why do people go to the snow?

   _____

3. Why do mountain climbers carry so much equipment?

   _____

4. Why do hikers like to reach very high altitudes?

   _____

5. Why do some mountain climbers use guides?

   _____

6. Why do people want to visit the Great Wall of China?

   _____

ELD Standard
Use more complex vocabulary and sentences appropriate for language arts and other content areas.
ELA Standard
Demonstrate appropriate English usage.

Name _____   Date _____

ⓐ Types of Adverbs

▬ ▬

✔ Adverbs are words that modify verbs, or tell how an action is done. There are adverbs of time, place, manner, and degree.

▬ ▬

■ Read the sentences. Then select the correct answer choice. Finally, write what kind of adverb each one is.

Example:

The orcas swam silently toward the shore.

What is the adverb?

☐ swam
☐ toward
☐ shore
☑ silently

What kind of adverb is it? _____ manner _____

1. We got to hear the humpback whales sing eerily.

   What is the adverb?

   ☐ whales
   ☐ eerily
   ☐ to hear
   ☐ sing

   What kind of adverb is it? _____

2. The dolphins swam behind the boat all day, to the delight of the people onboard.

   What is the adverb?

   ☐ all day
   ☐ delight
   ☐ people
   ☐ dolphins

   What kind of adverb is it? _____

3. We swim daily when we're staying at the beach.

   What is the adverb?

   ☐ beach
   ☐ we're
   ☐ swim
   ☐ daily

   What kind of adverb is it? _____

4. My brother loves to dive from the boat into the ocean.

   What is the adverb?

   ☐ loves
   ☐ ocean
   ☐ from the boat
   ☐ my

   What kind of adverb is it? _____

5. We looked the hotel room over completely before deciding to stay.

   What is the adverb?

   ☐ completely
   ☐ to
   ☐ hotel
   ☐ our

   What kind of adverb is it? _____

ELD Standard
   Identify and use parts of speech.
ELA Standard
   Identify and use adverbs.

227

■ In the chart below, make lists of the four types of adverbs used above.

Adverbs of Time	Adverbs of Place	Adverbs of Manner	Adverbs of Degree

Name _____   Date _____

b Phhrasal Verbs

━ ━ ━━ ━━ ━━ ━ ━━ ━━ ━━ ━━ ━━ ━━ ━━ ━ ━━ ━━ ━━ ━━ ━━

✔ Phrasal verbs are made up of at least two words. One is the main verb, and the other is usually a preposition.

━ ━ ━━ ━━ ━━ ━ ━━ ━━ ━━ ━━ ━━ ━━ ━━ ━ ━━ ━━ ━━ ━━ ━━

■ Read the boxes below with verbs and prepositions. Then write as many matches as you can for each verb in the space indicated. Finally, illustrate four of the phrases matched.

Example:

Verb: turn   **Preposition:** away

1. turn: turn away. _____

Verb	Preposition
turn	about
put	away
point	in
call	off
think	out
hand	over
figure	down
find	

1. turn: _____

2. put: _____

3. point: _____

4. call: _____

5. think: _____

6. hand: _____

7. figure: _____

8. find: _____

ELD Standard
    Identify and use parts of speech.
ELA Standard
    Identify all parts of speech.

Illustrations:

Phrase: _____

Phrase: _____

Phrase: _____

Phrase: _____

■ Can you think of more phrasal verbs? Write them in the space below.

_____   _____

_____   _____

_____   _____

Name _____   Date _____

a Suffixes

✔ Remember that a suffix is added to the end of a word and changes the word's part of speech.

■ Fill in the missing information to complete the chart below.

Verb	Noun (with Suffix –*ing*)	Person (with Suffix -*er*)
sprint		
	running	
		bowler
skateboard		
	skating	
		golfer
ski		
	dancing	

■ Illustrate two of the words from the third column.

Word: _____

Word: _____

ELD Standard
   Apply knowledge of word relationships, such as roots and affixes.
ELA Standard
   Use knowledge of prefixes and suffixes to determine the meaning of words.

231

Name _____   Date _____

b Pros and Cons

- Read the word at the top of each box. Then write one *pro* and one *con* about each sport in the proper spaces.

Example: racquetball

Pro: It is excellent exercise.

Con: You have to have access to a racquetball court.

Scuba Diving

Pro: _____

Con: _____

Skydiving

Pro: _____

Con: _____

Skiing

Pro: _____

Con: _____

Hiking

Pro: _____

Con: _____

ELD Standard
Use more complex vocabulary and sentences appropriate for language arts and other content areas.
ELA Standard
Support all statements and claims with anecdotes, descriptions, facts and statistics, and specific examples.

Name   Date

a Action Verbs

- Fill in the word webs by providing verbs that describe each sport.

Ping Pong

Basketball

Volleyball

Gymnastics

Cycling

ELD Standard
Understand and follow simple written directions for classroom-related activities.
ELA Standard
Demonstrate appropriate English usage.

233

Name _____   Date _____

b Habitual Past Tense

━━ ━━ ━━ ━━ ━━ ━━ ━━ ━━ ━━ ━━ ━━ ━━ ━━ ━━ ━━

✓ *Would* and *used to* are helping verbs that are used to describe things that happened on a regular basis in the past.

Example: We always *used to* attend the hayride and pumpkin gathering festival.

━━ ━━ ━━ ━━ ━━ ━━ ━━ ━━ ━━ ━━ ━━ ━━ ━━ ━━ ━━

▪ Write sentences about yourself based on the prompts.

Games you played in the past:

1. I used to play _____

2. _____

3. _____

People you knew in the past:

1. _____

2. _____

3. _____

Places you have gone regularly:

1. _____

2. _____

3. _____

Stores you shopped at in the past:

1. _____

2. _____

3. _____

Books that were your favorites:

1. _____

2. _____

3. _____

ELD Standard
Produce independent writing with consistent use of capitalization and periods, and correct spelling.
ELA Standard
Identify all parts of speech.

Name _____   Date _____

a Onomatopoeia

— —

✔ Onomatopoeia is the use of words that sound like the sounds they name.

Example: **Zip!**

— —

▪ Use each of the following words from the box in sentences. Then choose four to illustrate, indicating each one in the box.

Example: **The explosion made a big "boom!"**

whoosh	trickle	splat	zip	plop
smack	boom	zoom	slap	gurgle

1. _____

2. _____

3. _____

4. _____

5. _____

6. _____

7. _____

8. _____

9. _____

10. _____

ELD Standard
Apply knowledge of common English morphemes in oral and silent reading to derive meaning from literature and texts in content areas.
ELA Standard
Apply knowledge of word origins to determine the meaning of words and phrases.

Word: _____

Word: _____

Word: _____

Word: _____

Name _____   Date _____

b Writing a Composition

- Study the following themes from the box below. Then choose one and write a fantasy of at least one paragraph of four sentences, describing it. Use a topic sentence in each paragraph, as well as independent and dependent clauses.

| Sailing Ship | Eagle | Unicorn | Spaceship |

Title: _____

_____

_____

_____

_____

_____

_____

_____

_____

_____

_____

_____

_____

_____

_____

_____

_____

_____

_____

_____

ELD Standard
Proceed through the writing process to write short paragraphs that contain support details about a given topic.
ELA Standard
Demonstrate the mechanics of writing and appropriate English usage.

Name _____   Date _____

a The Word *Would*

▬ ▬ ▬ ▬ ▬ ▬ ▬ ▬ ▬ ▬ ▬ ▬ ▬ ▬ ▬ ▬ ▬ ▬

✔ The word *would* can be used in polite requests and offers.

Example: *Would* you like to go to the circus with me?
        Yes, I *would*.

▬ ▬ ▬ ▬ ▬ ▬ ▬ ▬ ▬ ▬ ▬ ▬ ▬ ▬ ▬ ▬ ▬ ▬

▪ Read the following descriptions of situations. Then formulate polite questions and answers to go with them, as in the following example. Underline the word *would* in each case.

Example:

You want to invite your mother to go to have ice cream with you.

Question: _____ <u>Would</u> you like to go have ice cream with me? _____

Answer: _____ Yes, I <u>would</u> love to go have ice cream with you. _____

1. You want to ask your best friend to come to your house for a barbecue.

   Question: _____

   Answer: _____

2. You want to ask your teacher to correct your paper.

   Question: _____

   Answer: _____

3. You want to invite your classmates to come watch you perform in a play.

   Question: _____

   Answer: _____

4. You want to ask your customers what they want help with.

   Question: _____

   Answer: _____

ELD Standard
  Produce independent writing with consistent use of capitalization and periods, and correct spelling.
ELA Standard
  Identify types and structure of sentences.

5. You want to ask if you can get a same-day appointment to see the doctor.

   Question: _____

   Answer: _____

6. You want to know if your guest wants whipped cream in his hot chocolate.

   Question: _____

   Answer: _____

Name   Date

b Suffixes/Writing an Informational Essay

✔ The suffix *-ist* can be used to form nouns that name people who participate in sports. It can also be used for certain occupations and jobs. In this sense, it means *the one who*.

■ Complete the following chart, writing the noun form that names the corresponding profession by adding the suffix *-ist* to the ending. Some words may need other spelling changes before adding *-ist*. Consult a dictionary if you are not sure about the spelling of the word with *-ist*.

Word	Profession
bicycle	
pharmacy	
sociology	
psychology	
environmental	
special	
biology	
percussion	
therapy	

ELD Standard
Collect information from various sources.
ELA Standard
Convey clear and accurate perspectives on the subject.

■ Following the process in the Writing Checklist, choose a word from one of the two columns above and write an informational essay about it. You may want to consult an encyclopedia, dictionary, or online resources to research your topic.

Title: _____

_____

_____

_____

_____

_____

_____

_____

_____

_____

_____

_____

_____

_____

_____

_____

_____

_____

_____

_____

_____

Name   Date

a Abstract Nouns

✔ Abstract nouns are words that represent ideas and concepts. These nouns are always singular.

reason	joy	confusion	kindness
bravery	trust	safety	peace
fairness	happiness	anger	friendship
progress	trouble	courage	information

■ Read the words from the box. Use eight of them in complete sentences on the lines below. Be sure the sentence brings out the meaning of the abstract noun.

1. _____

2. _____

3. _____

4. _____

5. _____

6. _____

7. _____

8. _____

■ Think of other abstract nouns and write them in the boxes. You might want to work with a partner or a small group to complete this activity.

_____	_____	_____

_____	_____

ELD Standard
Use more complex vocabulary and sentences appropriate for language arts and other content areas.
ELA Standard
Know abstract, and use this knowledge to analyze the meaning of complex words.

Name _____   Date _____

b Quotation Marks and Foreign Expressions

━━ ━━ ━━ ━━ ━━ ━━ ━━ ━━ ━━ ━━ ━━ ━━ ━━ ━━ ━━ ━━ ━━ ━━

✔ Quotation marks can be used to set apart words in a sentence. This is done when you provide the meaning of another word, often a word from another language, as in the example.

✔ The words being defined are usually in italics, or if the sentence is handwritten, they are underscored for italics.

Example: Mabel insisted on receiving *"per diem"* pay.

━━ ━━ ━━ ━━ ━━ ━━ ━━ ━━ ━━ ━━ ━━ ━━ ━━ ━━ ━━ ━━ ━━ ━━

▪ Look up each of the following foreign expressions in the dictionary. Once you know the meaning of the expression, write it in the space indicated, and use it in a complete sentence with appropriate punctuation.

1. enfant terrible

   Meaning: _____

   Sentence: _____

2. ex libris

   Meaning: _____

   Sentence: _____

3. comme il faut

   Meaning: _____

   Sentence: _____

4. au revoir

   Meaning: _____

   Sentence: _____

5. par excellence

   Meaning: _____

   Sentence: _____

6. vox populi

   Meaning: _____

   Sentence: _____

ELD Standard
Use a standard dictionary to determine the meaning of unknown words.
ELA Standard
Recognize the origins and meanings of frequently used foreign words in English and use these words accurately in speaking and writing.

Name _____   Date _____

a Appositives

━━ ━━ ━━ ━━ ━━ ━━ ━━ ━━ ━━ ━━ ━━ ━━ ━━ ━━ ━━ ━━ ━━ ━━ ━━

✔ Appositives are phrases in a sentence that rename the noun or pronoun before them. Commas are used to set appositives apart from the rest of the sentence.

Example: Mahatma Gandhi, the great Indian who practiced nonviolence, fought for his country's independence from Great Britain.

━━ ━━ ━━ ━━ ━━ ━━ ━━ ━━ ━━ ━━ ━━ ━━ ━━ ━━ ━━ ━━ ━━ ━━ ━━

■ Look at the information in each box. Write a sentence with an appositive phrase for each one, using the information provided.

> Name: Marian Anderson
> Occupation: singer
> Accomplishment: first black person to join the Metropolitan Opera in N.Y.

_____

_____

> Name: Susan B. Anthony
> Occupation: women's rights leader
> Accomplishment: helped women get the right to vote

_____

_____

> Name: John Glenn
> Occupation: astronaut
> Accomplishment: one of America's original seven astronauts

_____

_____

ELD Standard
  Edit writing for basic conventions.
ELA Standard
  Demonstrate the mechanics of writing.

■ Read the following sentences. Each one contains an appositive, but is missing the correct punctuation. Rewrite the sentences on the lines provided, including all necessary punctuation.

1. The people of Montgomery who undertook a bus boycott eventually triumphed.

_____

_____

2. The public facilities all segregated by color were eventually opened up to all people.

_____

_____

3. "Separate but equal" which was separate but not equal is fortunately a thing of the past.

_____

_____

4. Martin Luther King, Jr. the great civil rights leader did much to improve the lot of his people.

_____

_____

Name _____   Date _____

ᗷ Quotation Marks and Punctuation

✔ Quotation marks are used to show the exact words of a speaker. Quotation marks are put at the beginning and at the end of a quote. A comma is put before the quotation.

✔ Final punctuation goes inside the end quote.

✔ If the quotation is a full sentence, it starts with a capital letter. If it is just a phrase, it begins with a lowercase letter.

▪ Read the following sentences and determine whether the punctuation, including quotation marks, is correct. Mark the correct answer in the appropriate column. Then if the punctuation is incorrect, rewrite the sentence on the space indicated.

	Yes	No
1. The woman asked the restaurant owner, May I please use your telephone"	❑	❑
_____		
2. The restaurant owner answered, "No, Ma'am. I'm afraid I can't let you."	❑	❑
_____		
3. The protestors all shouted, We want equal rights!	❑	❑
_____		
4. The child asked her mother, "How long will we have to wait for the bus"	❑	❑
_____		
5. His mother answered, "The bus should be coming in about ten minutes."	❑	❑
_____		

ELD Standard
  Edit writing for grammatical structures and the mechanics of writing.
ELA Standard
  Use quotation marks around the exact words of a speaker.

Write five more sentences with direct quotations, using some of the words from the box.

boycott	arrest	separate	jail	nonviolent	bus

1. _____

2. _____

3. _____

4. _____

5. _____

Name   Date

a Capitalization of Proper Nouns

✔ The names of neighborhoods, institutions, historic movements, and book titles are capitalized because they are proper nouns.

■ Complete the following chart, writing the proper nouns using correct capitalization.

Proper Noun	Correct Capitalization
stanford medical center	
lincoln monument	
u.s. house of representatives	
supreme court	
women's rights movement	
boston college	
harlem	
uncle tom's cabin	
peace corps	
great depression	
library of congress	
gone with the wind	

ELD Standard
    Proceed through the writing process to write short paragraphs that contain supporting details about a given topic.
ELA Standard
    Use correct capitalization.

■ Look up two of the items from previous activity in an encyclopedia. Write a paragraph about each one, using topic sentences and supporting details.

Title: _____

_____

_____

_____

_____

_____

Title: _____

_____

_____

_____

_____

_____

Name _____   Date _____

b Punctuation of Book Titles

━━ ━ ━━ ━━ ━ ━━ ━ ━ ━━ ━━ ━ ━ ━━ ━━ ━ ━━ ━━ ━━ ━ ━━ ━

✔ The words making up book titles are always capitalized, except for the articles and prepositions. Book titles are always in italic letters. In handwriting, book titles are underlined to indicate italics.

✔ Publication dates follow the title, separated from it by a comma.

━━ ━ ━━ ━━ ━ ━━ ━ ━ ━━ ━━ ━ ━ ━━ ━━ ━ ━━ ━━ ━━ ━ ━━ ━

▪ Write the following book titles and publication dates, using correct capitalization and punctuation. Underline the words that should be italicized.

1. Leonardo: Italian genius 1987

   _____

2. Abraham lincoln a great president and man 1999

   _____

3. freedom is a long, hard road 1986

   _____

4. the price I paid to be me 2004

   _____

5. where did all the great ideas go 1990

   _____

6. great inventions by people under 14 2000

   _____

7. the wildest photographs of 1999 2000

   _____

8. why me 1976

   _____

9. I've got you covered—at least for now 2001

   _____

ELD Standard
   Edit writing for basic conventions.
ELA Standard
   Use underlining, quotation marks, or italics to identify titles of documents.

10. life's not fair but it sure is interesting 2003

_____

■ Find four books in the classroom or the library and write their titles and publication dates, using correct punctuation.

1. _____

2. _____

3. _____

4. _____

Name _____   Date _____

ⓐ Reflexive Pronouns

■ Reflexive pronouns are used when the subject of the sentence is also the direct object of the verb. A reflexive pronoun is used in the place of a direct object.

■ The reflexive pronouns are: *myself, yourself, itself, ourselves, himself, herself,* and *themselves.*

Example: Lucy Park trusted *herself* when it came to knowing how to take care of the elderly man.

Lucy Park = subject; **herself** = reflexive pronoun

■ Read the sentences below. Circle the subject and underline the reflexive pronoun in each one.

1. The team members congratulated themselves on a game well played.

2. Magic Johnson chided himself for missing the shot.

3. I always tell myself to stay calm when I'm about to play baseball.

4. Tiger Woods whispered to himself, "Come on, you can do it!"

5. We always tell ourselves that we can win the championship.

6. Did you hear the teacher remind herself to grade all the tests after school?

7. The dog licked itself after getting scratched on the fence.

8. After their workout, all the swimmers dried themselves off before getting dressed.

9. My best friend told me to stop talking to myself!

■ Fill in the blank with the appropriate reflexive pronoun to complete the sentences.

1. My grandmother and grandfather taught _____ to speak Italian.

2. Did you get mad at _____ when you forgot your homework?

3. You should always be good to _____ and get plenty of sleep!

4. The young boys taught _____ to play baseball in the streets of their villages.

ELD Standard
Use correct parts of speech.
ELA Standard
Make clear references between pronouns and antecedents.

Name _____   Date _____

b Capitalization of Proper Nouns

━━ ━━ ━━ ━━ ━━ ━━ ━━ ━━ ━━ ━━ ━━ ━━ ━━ ━━ ━━ ━━ ━━

✔ The names of professional teams, athletic organizations, and official competitions are capitalized because they are proper nouns.

Example: The Los Angeles Lakers = professional team

National Football League = athletic organization

World Series = official competition

━━ ━━ ━━ ━━ ━━ ━━ ━━ ━━ ━━ ━━ ━━ ━━ ━━ ━━ ━━ ━━ ━━

■ Complete the following chart, writing the proper nouns with correct capitalization.

Proper Nouns	Correct Capitalization
miami dolphins	
world cup	
nba playoffs	
national soccer association	
oakland athletics	
stanley cup	
new york marathon	

■ Complete each box by providing the names of professional teams, athletic organizations, and official competitions.

Professional Teams	Athletic Organizations	Official Competitions

ELD Standard
    Edit for basic conventions.
ELA Standard
    Use correct capitalization.

253

Name _____   Date _____

a Acronyms

━━ ━━ ━━ ━━ ━━ ━━ ━━ ━━ ━━ ━━ ━━ ━━ ━━ ━━ ━━ ━━ ━━

✔ Acronyms are words made up of the first letters of each of a group of words.

   Example: USA = United States of America

━━ ━━ ━━ ━━ ━━ ━━ ━━ ━━ ━━ ━━ ━━ ━━ ━━ ━━ ━━ ━━ ━━

■ Write the groups of words that the following acronyms stand for. If you need help, use a computer search engine to locate an acronym-finder, where you can look up many types of acronyms.

1. BART _____

2. RAM _____

3. NYPD _____

4. AWOL _____

5. ANA _____

6. NIMBY _____

7. SWAT _____

8. VOA _____

9. USNA _____

10. FAA _____

11. FAQ _____

12. SAC _____

13. PBS _____

ELD Standard
   Use decoding skills and knowledge of academic and social vocabulary to achieve independent reading.
ELA Standard
   Use correct capitalization.

■ Write the acronym for each of the following groups of words.

1. Global Broadcasting System _____

2. University of California at Berkeley _____

3. liquid crystal display _____

4. Environmental Protection Agency _____

5. blind carbon copy _____

6. the year 2000 _____

Name _____   Date _____

b Proverbs

━━ ━━ ━━ ━━ ━━ ━━ ━━ ━━ ━━ ━━ ━━ ━━ ━━ ━━ ━━ ━━

✔ Proverbs are condensed, but memorable sayings that embody some important fact or experience that is taken as true by many people.

Example: **A bird in the hand is worth two in the bush.**

Meaning: It's better to accept something that you have now than to try to get something better that you might not be able to get.

━━ ━━ ━━ ━━ ━━ ━━ ━━ ━━ ━━ ━━ ━━ ━━ ━━ ━━ ━━ ━━

▪ What do the following proverbs mean? Use the Internet to locate a proverb-finder, if you need help figuring out the meanings. Use your own words to tell how you would explain the meaning of the following proverbs to a person who had never heard them.

1. A fool and his money are soon parted.

   Meaning: _____

2. A man is known by the company he keeps.

   Meaning: _____

3. All that glitters is not gold.

   Meaning: _____

4. Beauty is only skin-deep.

   Meaning: _____

5. Haste makes waste.

   Meaning: _____

6. The only way to have a friend is to be one.

   Meaning: _____

7. You never miss the water until the well runs dry.

   Meaning: _____

8. The pen is mightier than the sword.

   Meaning: _____

ELD Standard
Use the text to draw inferences and conclusions and make generalizations.
ELA Standard
Understand and explain the figurative and metaphorical use of words in contexts.

9. More than enough is too much.

    Meaning: _____

10. Love me, love my dog.

    Meaning: _____

11. Let your conscience be your guide.

    Meaning: _____

12. Knowledge is power.

    Meaning: _____

13. Home is where you hang your hat.

    Meaning: _____

14. Everything comes to him who waits.

    Meaning: _____

15. Don't throw pearls before swine.

    Meaning: _____

Name   Date

a Capitalization of Official Titles

✔ Official titles are capitalized when they refer to specific people.

Example: secretary of transportation Norman Mineta
              Secretary of Transportation Norman Mineta

■ Complete the chart below writing all the proper nouns with correct capitalization.

Proper Noun	Correct Capitalization
dr. kraft	
governor adams	
mayor hernandez	
princess caroline of monaco	
sergeant romero	
general colin powell	
speaker frist	
secretary general kofi annan	
king hussein	
ambassador greenfield	
vice president gore	
president kennedy	
first lady laura bush	

ELD Standard
    Edit writing for basic conventions.
ELA Standard
    Use correct capitalization.

Name _____   Date _____

b Demonstrating Comprehension

▬▬ ▬▬ ▬▬ ▬▬ ▬▬ ▬▬ ▬▬ ▬▬ ▬▬ ▬▬ ▬▬ ▬▬ ▬▬ ▬▬

■ Read the following box with information about the life of Mother Teresa. Then answer the comprehension questions that follow by marking the correct answer choice.

Highlights of Mother Teresa's Life

Maiden name: Agnes Gonxhe Bojaxhiu

Birthplace: Skopje, Yugoslavia (present-day Macedonia)

Residence: Calcutta, India

1910 Was born on August 17.

1928 Went to India to teach at a convent school in Calcutta.

1937 Took final vows in the convent.

1948 Left the convent to work in Calcutta slums. Received some medical training in Paris.

1950 Started the Missionaries of Charity.

1952 Opened the House for the Dying.

1957 The Missionaries of Charity started work with lepers and in many disaster areas of the world.

1971 Was awarded the Pope John XXIII Peace Prize.

1979 Was awarded the Nobel Peace Prize.

1997 Died on September 5.

---

1. Where was Mother Teresa born?
   - ☐ Calcutta, India
   - ☐ Paris, France
   - ☐ Skopje, Yugoslavia
   - ☐ None of the above.

2. What did Mother Teresa do in 1937?
   - ☐ She started the Missionaries of Charity.
   - ☐ She took her final vows in the convent.
   - ☐ She won a humanitarian award.
   - ☐ None of the above.

3. What prize did she win in 1971?
   - ☐ The Nobel Peace Prize.
   - ☐ The Time Person of the Year Prize
   - ☐ The Pope John XXIII Peace Prize
   - ☐ All of the above.

4. What happened in 1948 in Mother Teresa's life?
   - ☐ She got some medical training in Paris.
   - ☐ She began working in Calcutta slums.
   - ☐ None of the above.
   - ☐ The first two options.

5. Which of the dates below show the span of Mother Teresa's life?
   - ☐ 1948–1979
   - ☐ 1910–1971
   - ☐ 1948–1952
   - ☐ 1910–1997

6. Why did Mother Teresa go to Calcutta?
   - ☐ To teach at a convent school.
   - ☐ So she could win the Pope John XXIII Peace Prize.
   - ☐ To get some medical training.
   - ☐ None of the above.

ELD Standard
Write responses to selected literature that exhibit understanding of the text, using detailed sentences and transitions.
ELA Standard
Develop interpretations exhibiting careful reading, understanding, and insight.

■ Read the following excerpt from Mother Teresa's Nobel Peace Prize acceptance speech. Write a paragraph on the lines below, giving your reactions to her words.

Mother Teresa's Nobel Peace Prize Acceptance Speech
Excerpt

I choose the poverty of our poor people. But I am grateful to receive (the Nobel) in the name of the hungry, the naked, the homeless, of the crippled, of the blind, of the lepers, of all those people who feel unwanted, unloved, uncared-for throughout society, people that have become a burden to the society and are shunned by everyone.

_____

_____

_____

_____

_____

_____

Name _____   Date _____

ⓐ Borrowed Words from Foreign Languages

━━ ━━ ━━ ━━ ━━ ━━ ━━ ━━ ━━ ━━ ━━ ━━ ━━ ━━ ━━ ━━ ━━ ━━

✔ Many terms in the areas of politics, war, and espionage are borrowed from other languages. There are also many other words in English that come from foreign languages.

━━ ━━ ━━ ━━ ━━ ━━ ━━ ━━ ━━ ━━ ━━ ━━ ━━ ━━ ━━ ━━ ━━ ━━

▪ Read the words that follow, then look them up in a dictionary. Write down what they mean, and then use each one in a sentence. The meaning for the first one is already done.

1. bon voyage

   Meaning: _____ Have a good trip. _____

   Sentence: _____

2. versus

   Meaning: _____

   Sentence: _____

3. sauté

   Meaning: _____

   Sentence: _____

4. risotto

   Meaning: _____

   Sentence: _____

5. résumé

   Meaning: _____

   Sentence: _____

6. raconteur

   Meaning: _____

   Sentence: _____

7. quasi

   Meaning: _____

   Sentence: _____

ELD Standard
Use a standard dictionary to determine the meaning of unknown words.
ELA Standard
Recognize the origins and meanings of frequently used foreign words in English and use these words accurately in speaking and writing.

8. maestro

Meaning: _____

Sentence: _____

9. mardi gras

Meaning: _____

Sentence: _____

10. vice versa

Meaning: _____

Sentence: _____

11. modus operandi

Meaning: _____

Sentence: _____

12. impasse

Meaning: _____

Sentence: _____

13. entrepreneur

Meaning: _____

Sentence: _____

14. a cappella

Meaning: _____

Sentence: _____

15. alma mater

Meaning: _____

Sentence: _____

Name _____   Date _____

b Vocabulary: Words Meaning

▬ ▬ ▬ ▬ ▬ ▬ ▬ ▬ ▬ ▬ ▬ ▬ ▬ ▬ ▬ ▬ ▬ ▬ ▬

■ Read the words in the following box. Then choose five of them and write the meanings of the terms in your own words. Use a dictionary if you need help with the meanings. Then write a sentence for each word.

negotiations	equality	racism
conspiracy	protest	poverty
segregation	justice	Civil Rights Movement

1. Meaning: _____

   Sentence: _____

2. Meaning: _____

   Sentence: _____

3. Meaning: _____

   Sentence: _____

4. Meaning: _____

   Sentence: _____

5. Meaning: _____

   Sentence: _____

ELD Standard
   Use more complex vocabulary and sentences appropriate for language arts and other content areas.
ELA Standard
   Use a dictionary to learn the meaning and other features of unknown words.

Name _____   Date _____

a Borrowed Words from Foreign Languages

■ Look up the following words in a dictionary. On the line beside each word, write the language that the word comes from.

1. mosquito _____

2. siesta _____

3. chutzpah _____

4. canyon _____

5. goulash _____

6. faux pas _____

7. aficionado _____

8. status quo _____

9. patio _____

10. terra firma _____

11. caudillo _____

12. verbatim _____

13. bona fide _____

14. parachute _____

15. metropolis _____

16. ukulele _____

17. chocolate _____

■ Complete the following chart choosing and writing four borrowed words from the last activity that are names of food.

Borrowed Word	Origin

ELD Standard
Organize and record information from selected literature and content areas by displaying it on pictures, lists, charts and tables.
ELA Standard
Apply knowledge of word origins, derivations, synonyms, antonyms, and idioms to determine the meaning of words and phrases.

Name _____ Date _____

b Cognates and False Cognates

✔ Cognates are words that are related to words in other languages. They sound alike, and most have the same or similar meaning. Words that sound alike but mean different things are called *false cognates*.

▪ Complete the following chart about cognates using a Spanish-English Dictionary. Write the meaning of those Spanish words that are false cognates in relation with the English words, and write "cognate" if the Spanish word is a cognate.

English Word	Spanish Word	Cognate / Meaning
actual	actual	
machine	máquina	
blank	blanco	
educated	educado	
international	internacional	
fabulous	fabuloso	
exit	éxito	
football	fútbol	
real	real	
telephone	teléfono	
carpenter	carpintero	
deception	decepción	
complicated	complicado	
rope	ropa	
soup	sopa	
success	suceso	
artist	artista	

ELD Standard
Identify cognates and false cognates in literature and texts in content areas.
ELA Standard
Clarify word meanings through the use of definitions, examples, restatement, or contrast.

- Think of five cognates and write them below.

1. _____

2. _____

3. _____

4. _____

5. _____

Name _____   Date _____

ⓐ Rhetorical Questions

▬▬ ▬▬ ▬▬ ▬▬ ▬▬ ▬▬ ▬▬ ▬▬ ▬▬ ▬▬ ▬▬ ▬▬ ▬▬ ▬▬ ▬▬

✔ A rhetorical question is one that the writer or speaker asks, but one to which a specific answer is not necessarily expected or needed.

✔ Rhetorical questions can be very effective as titles or as openings to essays.

　Example: *Who wants war?*

　　　　　 Since no one wants war, people may use this rhetorical question to explain why war may be inevitable.

▬▬ ▬▬ ▬▬ ▬▬ ▬▬ ▬▬ ▬▬ ▬▬ ▬▬ ▬▬ ▬▬ ▬▬ ▬▬ ▬▬ ▬▬

▪ Read each rhetorical question and explain in your own words when a speaker or writer may want to use it. You may want to look up rhetorical questions using an Internet search engine.

1. Who knew?

　_____

2. How can this be possible?

　_____

3. Can you beat that?

　_____

4. Who cares?

　_____

5. How should I know?

　_____

6. Do fish swim?

　_____

ELD Standard
　　Collect information from various sources.
ELA Standard
　　Identify types and structure of sentences.

Name _____   Date _____

b Reflective Writing

━ ━

✔ Reflective writing is a personal, informal way of writing. It tends to focus more on feelings and thoughts than on facts.

━ ━

▪ In the space provided below, write silently for 20 uninterrupted minutes. Try to write your thoughts just as they come to you. Try not to focus too much on your writing technique, but rather focus on your story. After you have finished writing, share your work with a classmate.

Prompt: Write about a time when you had to put your fears aside and act bravely.

ELD Standard
Narrate a sequence of events and communicate their significance to the audience.
ELA Standard
Write descriptions that use concrete sensory details to present and support unified impressions of people, places, things, or experiences.

Name _____   Date _____

a Passive Construction

━ ━

✔ A passive construction is used to make statements about a topic when it is impossible or unnecessary to state who is doing the action. A passive construction may be in any tense.

   Examples: **The Great Wall was built by many laborers.** (past)

   The Great Wall is maintained by a large number of workers. (present)

━ ━

■ Read the sentences below. Change them from the passive to the active construction.

1. Lance Armstrong was diagnosed with cancer by his doctor.

   _____

2. Chemotherapy was given to him to destroy the tumor.

   _____

3. Other cancer survivors are now being supported by Lance Armstrong.

   _____

4. Bicycling was taken up as a hobby by Lance Armstrong when he was very young.

   _____

5. The bicycle was hung from two hooks in the garage by Lance.

   _____

6. A brand new bicycle will be gotten by my best friend for her birthday.

   _____

ELD Standard
   Use more complex vocabulary and sentences appropriate for language arts and other content areas.
ELA Standard
   Identify types and structure of sentences.

269

Name   Date
_____   _____

b Writing an Essay

▬ ▬ ▬ ▬ ▬ ▬ ▬ ▬ ▬ ▬ ▬ ▬ ▬ ▬ ▬ ▬ ▬ ▬

Who do you admire? Do you have any heroes? What makes a hero?

▬ ▬ ▬ ▬ ▬ ▬ ▬ ▬ ▬ ▬ ▬ ▬ ▬ ▬ ▬ ▬ ▬ ▬

■ Visit the library and look up information on someone you would like to write an essay on. Write a three-paragraph essay, following the tips in the Writing Checklist. Begin by taking notes on information you find in encyclopedias, biographies, or Internet search engines. Use topic sentences and supporting details in your writing. When you are finished, share your essay with your classmates.

ELD Standard
Investigate and research a topic in a content area and develop a brief essay or report.
ELA Standard
Use strategies of notetaking, outlining, and summarizing to impose structure on composition drafts.

Name _____   Date _____

a Past Perfect Tense

▬ ▬

✔ You use the past perfect tense to tell about something that happened before something else in the past.

✔ The past perfect tense is formed by adding the helping verb *had* to the past participle of the main verb.

▬ ▬

■ Read the information from the following box. It tells some facts about San Francisco history in the form of a timeline. Then complete the sentences using the past perfect tense, following the example. Circle the words forming the past perfect tense in each sentence.

> **1769:** The entrance to the San Francisco Bay is discovered.
>
> **1776:** Presidio of San Francisco and Mission Dolores are founded.
>
> **1820:** Ships from Boston begin to visit the Spanish towns and missions along the coast.
>
> **1848:** Gold is discovered in California.
>
> **1849:** The California Gold Rush is underway.
>
> **1853:** The California Academy of Sciences is founded.
>
> **1860:** The Pony Express begins its first trip across the continent.
>
> **1892:** The Sierra Club is founded.
>
> **1906:** The San Francisco Earthquake and Fire.

Example:

Mariners knew how to enter San Francisco Bay because in 1769,

the entrance (had been discovered.)

1. Spanish missionaries now lived and worked in San Francisco, because in 1776,

   _____

2. Many people came to California in 1849, because in 1848,

   _____

3. In the 1860s, people could receive mail more quickly than ever before, because after 1860,

   _____

ELD Standard
Use common verbs, nouns, and high-frequency modifiers in writing simple sentences.
ELA Standard
Identify and properly use past perfect verb tense.

271

4. After 1820, people from Boston could be found in California, because

_____

5. Conservationists were able to fight to protect the boundaries of Yosemite National Park, because in 1892,

_____

6. Much of San Francisco was destroyed because in 1906,

_____

Name   Date

b Passive Structures

▬▬ ▬▬ ▬▬ ▬▬ ▬▬ ▬▬ ▬▬ ▬▬ ▬▬ ▬▬ ▬▬ ▬▬ ▬▬ ▬▬ ▬▬

✔ The passive structure is used when the doer of the action is either unimportant or unknown.

✔ The form of the helping verb *(to) be* must agree with the subject. If the subject is plural, *were* is used. If it is singular, *was* is used.

▬▬ ▬▬ ▬▬ ▬▬ ▬▬ ▬▬ ▬▬ ▬▬ ▬▬ ▬▬ ▬▬ ▬▬ ▬▬ ▬▬ ▬▬

■ Write sentences with the passive structure using the subjects and verbs provided below, as in the example.

Example:

Subject: concrete; **verb:** scatter

Concrete was scattered around the streets.

1. **Subject:** bridges; **verb:** retrofit

_____

2. **Subject:** hospitals; **verb:** fill

_____

3. **Subject:** bridge; **verb:** damage

_____

4. **Subject:** wall; **verb:** destroy

_____

5. **Subject:** cobblestone; **verb:** crack

_____

6. **Subject:** fire; **verb:** fight

_____

7. **Subject:** explosion; **verb:** hear

_____

8. **Subject:** damage; **verb:** repair

_____

ELD Standard
Use correct parts of speech, including correct verb–subject agreement.
ELA Standard
Identify subject and verb are in agreement.

273

9. **Subject:** streets; **verb:** protect

_____

10. **Subject:** emergency; **verb:** report

_____

Name   Date

a Uncountable Nouns

✔ There are many nouns that cannot be counted.

Example: *Ice* formed on my windshield. (weather)

Democracy is the choice of the people. (idea)

■ Fill in the boxes with uncountable nouns that fit the categories in each heading.

Weather

_____   _____   _____   _____

Ideas

_____   _____   _____   _____

■ Countable or uncountable? Read the following nouns and decide whether they are countable or uncountable. Check the appropriate box.

	Countable	Uncountable
1. glaciers	❑	❑
2. sleet	❑	❑
3. forest	❑	❑
4. rivers	❑	❑
5. clouds	❑	❑
6. wind	❑	❑
7. rainstorm	❑	❑

ELD Standard
    Identify and use parts of speech.
ELA Standard
    Identify and correctly use various parts of speech.

Name _____   Date _____

b Progression of Occurences

▬ ▬ ▬ ▬ ▬ ▬ ▬ ▬ ▬ ▬ ▬ ▬ ▬ ▬ ▬ ▬ ▬ ▬

■ Look up each of the following natural phenomena in an encyclopedia. Then write descriptive sentences about the progression of the following occurrences. The first one is already done.

Tsunami

Before: A natural impulsive disturbance, such as an earthquake, occurs. _____

During: This generates a series of waves in a body of water. _____

After: Coastlines are hit by the waves, causing severe damage. _____

Hurricane

Before: _____

During: _____

After: _____

Avalanche

Before: _____

During: _____

After: _____

Drought

Before: _____

During: _____

After: _____

ELD Standard
Collect information from various sources and take notes on a given topic.
ELA Standard
Convey clear and accurate perspectives on the subject.

Name _____   Date _____

ⓐ Past Perfect Tense

✔ The past perfect is used to describe an action that took place in the past before another action interrupted or changed it.

Examples: It <u>had rained</u> for two days before the sky finally cleared.

When the settlers arrived, the Native Americans <u>had</u> already <u>lived</u> here for centuries.

■ Use each of the phrases below in a complete sentence using the past perfect tense. The first one is already done.

1. had known

_____ My parents had known each other for six years before they got married. _____

2. had come back

_____

3. had taken root

_____

4. had been replanted

_____

5. had been reforested

_____

6. had been replaced

_____

7. had overcome

_____

8. had sprouted

_____

ELD Standard
Use common verbs, nouns, and high-frequency modifiers in writing simple sentences.
ELA Standard
Identify and properly use past perfect verb tense.

Name   Date

ⓑ Writing Captions

➖➖➖➖➖➖➖➖➖➖➖➖➖➖➖➖➖➖➖

✔ Captions are placed below or alongside photographs or pictures to describe the content of the picture.

➖➖➖➖➖➖➖➖➖➖➖➖➖➖➖➖➖➖➖

◼ Write an extended caption (two sentences) for each illustration. The first one is already done.

Caption

The family is gathered around the radio. They are listening to a show.

Caption

ELD Standard
Use common verbs, nouns, and high-frequency modifiers in writing simple sentences.
ELA Standard
Demonstrate the mechanics of writing and appropriate English usage.

Caption

_____

_____

Caption

_____

_____

Name _____   Date _____

a Prepositions

━━ ━━ ━━ ━━ ━━ ━━ ━━ ━━ ━━ ━━ ━━ ━━ ━━ ━━ ━━ ━━

✔ Prepositions tell about position. They link nouns or pronouns to another part of a sentence by describing relationships such as direction, location, or time.

Example: **The students are <u>in</u> the classroom.** (location)

━━ ━━ ━━ ━━ ━━ ━━ ━━ ━━ ━━ ━━ ━━ ━━ ━━ ━━ ━━ ━━

▪ Read each of the following prepositions. Mark in the appropriate column if the preposition is referring to direction (D), location (L), or time (T). Then use each of them to write a sentence.

	D	L	T			D	L	T
1. in	❑	❑	❑		6. beside	❑	❑	❑
2. under	❑	❑	❑		7. to	❑	❑	❑
3. during	❑	❑	❑		8. before	❑	❑	❑
4. across	❑	❑	❑		9. over	❑	❑	❑
5. since	❑	❑	❑		10. through	❑	❑	❑

1. _____

2. _____

3. _____

4. _____

5. _____

6. _____

7. _____

8. _____

9. _____

10. _____

ELD Standard
   Identify and use parts of speech.
ELA Standard
   Identify and use prepositions in writing and speaking.

Name _____   Date _____

b Writing a Fictional Story

- Write a fictional story about one of the following topics. Use different verb tenses and prepositions to enhance the descriptions in your writing.

hurricane	mudslide	drought	tornado

Title: _____

_____

_____

_____

_____

_____

_____

_____

_____

_____

_____

_____

_____

_____

_____

_____

_____

_____

_____

_____

_____

ELD Standard
Write in different genres, including coherent plot development, characterization, and setting.
ELA Standard
Develop a standard plot line and point of view.

Name _____   Date _____

a Participial Phrases

— — — — — — — — — — — — — — — — —

✔ Participial phrases are made up of a participle and its object (or complement) and modifiers. It functions as an *adjective*, modifying a noun or pronoun.

Examples: <u>Absorbed in the chaos of the aftermath of the earthquake</u>, I completely forgot where I parked my car.

Anil, <u>showing more caution than bravado</u>, stayed at higher ground until the flash flood warnings were called off.

The children nervously watched the hurricane blowing outside, <u>alarmed by its ferocity</u>.

— — — — — — — — — — — — — — — — —

■ Read the sentences below and underline the participial phrase. Then circle the noun it modifies.

1. Having returned to their battered neighborhood, the families set to work on cleaning up.

2. The paramedics, exhausted from hours of life-saving work, slept at the station.

3. After gaining in strength, the storm pounded the small island.

4. The wind, full of sand and debris, whipped through the village with a fury.

5. The mobile homes, torn apart by the tornado that passed through the region, lay in pieces on the ground.

6. Completely flooded by the river, the old school had to be rebuilt.

7. The pipes, frozen solid during the raging storm, burst and caused extensive damage to the cabin.

ELD Standard
   Identify and use parts of speech.
ELA Standard
   Identify and use participles.

Name _____   Date _____

b Homophones

━ ━ ━ ━ ━ ━ ━ ━ ━ ━ ━ ━ ━ ━ ━ ━ ━ ━ ━

✔ Homophones are words that sound alike, but are spelled differently and have different meanings.

━ ━ ━ ━ ━ ━ ━ ━ ━ ━ ━ ━ ━ ━ ━ ━ ━ ━ ━

▪ Look at the illustrations. Then look at the pair of words and circle the correct homophone that corresponds to the image.

Hare   Hair

Tale   Tail

Four   For

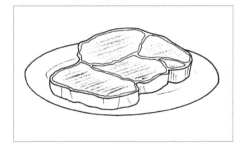

Meat   Meet

Night   Knight

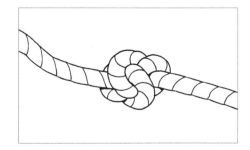

Not   Knot

ELD Standard
Demonstrate comprehension of simple vocabulary with an appropriate action.
ELA Standard
Use knowledge of homophones to determine meanings of words.

Name   Date
_____   _____

a Adjectives with One or More Syllables

▬ ▬ ▬ ▬ ▬ ▬ ▬ ▬ ▬ ▬ ▬ ▬ ▬ ▬ ▬ ▬ ▬ ▬ ▬ ▬

✔ Adjectives with a single syllable, usually come before those with more than one syllable when they are used in a sentence.

▬ ▬ ▬ ▬ ▬ ▬ ▬ ▬ ▬ ▬ ▬ ▬ ▬ ▬ ▬ ▬ ▬ ▬ ▬ ▬

■ Write sentences using the adjectives and nouns provided, as in the example.

Example:

Adjectives: large, spinning; **noun:** tornado

The large, spinning tornado approached the town.
_____

1. **Adjectives:** bright, shiny; **noun:** necklace

_____

2. **Adjectives:** green, gigantic; **noun:** landscape

_____

3. **Adjectives:** striped, gorgeous; **noun:** fabric

_____

4. **Adjectives:** happy, magnificent; **noun:** celebration

_____

5. **Adjectives:** round, nutritious; **noun:** vegetables

_____

6. **Adjectives:** rare, beautiful; **noun:** gemstone

_____

7. **Adjectives:** vast, hilly; **noun:** countryside

_____

8. **Adjectives:** brown, curly; **noun:** hair

_____

ELD Standard
    Identify and use parts of speech.
ELA Standard
    Place modifiers properly.

9. **Adjectives:** huge, modern; **noun:** bridge

_____

10. **Adjectives:** faint, whispering; **noun:** breeze

_____

■ What is the proper order of the following sets of adjectives? Number them on the lines provided. The first one is already done.

stormy	__2__	cold	__1__
awesome	_____	powerful	_____
indestructible	_____	old	_____
thin	_____	fragile	_____
injured	_____	trapped	_____
straight	_____	narrow	_____
tropical	_____	mild	_____
strong	_____	disastrous	_____

Name _____   Date _____

b Writing a Poem

■ Write short poems about the topics in the boxes below. Use your imagination when choosing adjectives for your poems. You may use a thesaurus or Internet search engines to find descriptive words. The poems don't need to rhyme and they don't need to use correct grammar.

Rainy Days

_____

_____

_____

_____

_____

The First Snow

_____

_____

_____

_____

_____

_____

The Long Days of Summer

_____

_____

_____

_____

_____

_____

ELD Standard
    Use appropriate language variations and genres in writing for language arts and other content areas.
ELA Standard
    Use a thesaurus to identify alternative word choices and meanings.

Name _____ Date _____

a Antonyms

✔ Antonyms are words that have opposite meanings.

Example: **beautiful—ugly**

■ Write the antonym for each word below.

1. increase   _____

2. cool   _____

3. weak   _____

4. violent   _____

5. expand   _____

6. descend   _____

7. dry   _____

8. straight   _____

9. float   _____

10. winter   _____

11. thaw   _____

■ Choose two pairs of antonyms above and illustrate them in the boxes below. Write the words on the lines provided.

ELD Standard
Recognize simple antonyms and synonyms in written text. Expand recognition of them and begin to use appropriately.
ELA Standard
Understand and explain common antonyms and synonyms.

Name _____   Date _____

b Gerunds

━━ ━━ ━━ ━━ ━━ ━━ ━━ ━━ ━━ ━━ ━━ ━━ ━━ ━━ ━━ ━━ ━━ ━━ ━━

✔ Gerunds are verbs that end in *-ing* and are used as nouns. Gerunds can be the subject, direct object, and other parts of the sentence.

━━ ━━ ━━ ━━ ━━ ━━ ━━ ━━ ━━ ━━ ━━ ━━ ━━ ━━ ━━ ━━ ━━ ━━ ━━

■ Circle or highlight the gerund in each sentence. Write the verb that the gerund comes from on the line below each sentence.

Example:

(Riding) her bike at full speed, Rebecca got home earlier than usual.

_____ To ride _____

1. Wishing for a good grade on the science test, Magda sharpened her pencil and began working.

   _____

2. Flying low over the homes, people on the airliner could see the pools in the backyards.

   _____

3. Expecting to see her mother waiting for her after school, Luisa was surprised to see her grandfather there.

   _____

4. Recalling the last time his team won the championship, Paco could hardly wait for the last game to start.

   _____

5. Forgetting everything they had ever been taught about sunburns, the kids played in the sun without putting on their sunscreen.

   _____

6. Washing her gym shirt late Sunday evening, Lorena hoped it would be dry by morning.

   _____

7. Falling on the ground in glorious color, the autumn leaves continue to come down.

   _____

ELD Standard
   Identify and use parts of speech.
ELA Standard
   Identify and correctly use various parts of speech.

8. Volunteering to help the new boy in class, Victor introduced himself to Frankie.

   _____

9. Deciding against attending baseball camp, Hector instead chose basketball camp.

   _____

■ Think of five other gerunds and use them in complete sentences below. Circle or highlight the gerund in each sentence.

1. _____

2. _____

3. _____

4. _____

5. _____

Name _____   Date _____

a *So-That* Sentences

▬ ▬ ▬ ▬ ▬ ▬ ▬ ▬ ▬ ▬ ▬ ▬ ▬ ▬ ▬ ▬ ▬ ▬

✔ The word *so* can be used in the same way as the word *very*. It is used to express a high degree of a particular quality.

▬ ▬ ▬ ▬ ▬ ▬ ▬ ▬ ▬ ▬ ▬ ▬ ▬ ▬ ▬ ▬ ▬

■ Complete the *so-that* sentences below. Follow the example.

Example:

   It was so <u>hot that you could fry an egg on the sidewalk</u>.

1. It was so dry that _____.

2. It was so _____ that the farmer had to pick his crops early.

3. It is _____ cold _____ I need to wear a hat and gloves.

4. I am so _____ that I think I could eat two dinners!

5. _____ that she drank three glasses of water in a row!

6. It was so windy that _____.

7. It was so _____ that _____.

8. I was so _____ that I simply crawled into bed and fell asleep.

9. The brothers were so _____that they _____.

10. The show was so funny that _____.

11. Both girls were so clumsy that_____.

12. The last book I read was so _____ that I want to read it again sometime.

13. You were so _____ yesterday that _____.

14. She waited so long to respond to the invitation that _____.

ELD Standard
   Edit and correct basic grammatical structures and usage of the conventions of writing.
ELA Standard
   Identify types and structure of sentences.

Name   Date
_____   _____

b Writing Bulleted Lists

▬ ▬ ▬ ▬ ▬ ▬ ▬ ▬ ▬ ▬ ▬ ▬ ▬ ▬ ▬ ▬ ▬ ▬

✔ Whenever you are going to write about something or when you need to remember things, you can make a bulleted list.

▬ ▬ ▬ ▬ ▬ ▬ ▬ ▬ ▬ ▬ ▬ ▬ ▬ ▬ ▬ ▬ ▬ ▬

■ Read the topics below from each box and create bulleted list of items to go with each one.

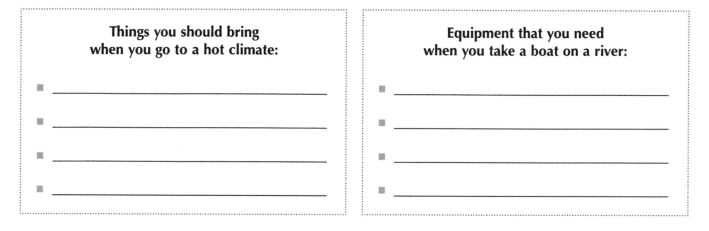

**Things you should bring
when you go to a hot climate:**

■ _____

■ _____

■ _____

■ _____

**Equipment that you need
when you take a boat on a river:**

■ _____

■ _____

■ _____

■ _____

Things to do to be a good student:

■ _____

■ _____

■ _____

■ _____

How you can help people in your community:

■ _____

■ _____

■ _____

■ _____

ELD Standard
    Organize and record information from selected literature and content areas by displaying it on pictures, lists, charts, and tables.
ELA Standard
    Use a variety of effective and coherent organizational patterns.

Name _____   Date _____

ⓐ Closed and Open Compound Nouns

▬ ▬ ▬ ▬ ▬ ▬ ▬ ▬ ▬ ▬ ▬ ▬ ▬ ▬ ▬ ▬ ▬ ▬

✔ Some nouns in English are made from putting two words together. These are called *closed compound nouns*.

✔ Other compound nouns are made from two separate words and are called *open compound nouns*.

▬ ▬ ▬ ▬ ▬ ▬ ▬ ▬ ▬ ▬ ▬ ▬ ▬ ▬ ▬ ▬ ▬ ▬

▪ Use a dictionary to determine whether the following words make an open or closed compound noun when put together by checking the correct box.

		Open	Closed
Example:			
mud + slide = mudslide		☐	☑
1. wild + fire = _____		☐	☐
2. post + office = _____		☐	☐
3. over + coat = _____		☐	☐
4. water + proof = _____		☐	☐
5. main + land = _____		☐	☐
6. high + school = _____		☐	☐
7. pan + cake = _____		☐	☐
8. skate + board = _____		☐	☐
9. hand + ball = _____		☐	☐
10. ear + phone = _____		☐	☐
11. toad + stool = _____		☐	☐

ELD Standard
Use a standard dictionary to determine meaning of unknown words.
ELA Standard
Spell correctly compound words.

Name _____   Date _____

b Giving Tips

▬ ▬ ▬ ▬ ▬ ▬ ▬ ▬ ▬ ▬ ▬ ▬ ▬ ▬ ▬ ▬ ▬ ▬ ▬

■ Read the topics from the boxes below. Then make a list of tips you might give to someone, if asked.

How to prepare for a test:

1. Re-read your textbook. _____

2. _____

3. _____

4. _____

How to be a good friend:

1. _____

2. _____

3. _____

4. _____

How to clean the kitchen:

1. _____

2. _____

3. _____

4. _____

How to care for your pet dog:

1. _____

2. _____

3. _____

4. _____

ELD Standard
Write more complex vocabulary and sentences appropriate for language arts and other content areas.
ELA Standard
Revise writing to improve organization and word choice after checking the logic of the ideas and the precision of the vocabulary.

Name _____   Date _____

◧ Using a Dictionary/Synonyms and Antonyms

▬▬ ▬▬ ▬▬ ▬▬ ▬▬ ▬▬ ▬▬ ▬▬ ▬▬ ▬▬ ▬▬ ▬▬ ▬▬ ▬▬

■ Look up each of the following words in the dictionary and write its definition.

crash	lifeboat	steamship	shiver	rescue
iceberg	passenger	voyage	fancy	disaster

Definitions:

1. _____

2. _____

3. _____

4. _____

5. _____

6. _____

7. _____

8. _____

9. _____

10. _____

▬▬ ▬▬ ▬▬ ▬▬ ▬▬ ▬▬ ▬▬ ▬▬ ▬▬ ▬▬ ▬▬ ▬▬ ▬▬ ▬▬

■ Can you find...

1. a synonym for the word *rescue?*   _____

2. a synonym for the word *crash?*   _____

3. an antonym for the word *fancy?*   _____

4. a synonym for the word *voyage?*   _____

5. a synonym for the word *shiver?*   _____

ELD Standard
  Use a standard dictionary to determine meaning of unknown words.
ELA Standard
  Use a thesaurus to determine related words and concepts.

Name _____   Date _____

b Organizing your Ideas

— — — — — — — — — — — — — — — — — — — —

■ Read the following list of accidents and disasters. Then, in the spaces provided, write your ideas about the causes, effects, and safety precautions that can be used to avoid such disasters.

Bicycle accidents:

Causes: _____

Effects: _____

Safety precautions: _____

_____

Falling down the stairs:

Causes: _____

Effects: _____

Safety precautions: _____

_____

Drowning in a swimming pool:

Causes: _____

Effects: _____

Safety precautions: _____

_____

ELD Standard
Produce independent writing with consistent use of capitalization, periods, and correct spelling.
ELA Standard
Demonstrate the mechanics of writing and appropriate English usage.

Getting lost while hiking:

Causes: _____

Effects: _____

Safety precautions: _____

_____

Accidents in a science laboratory:

Causes: _____

Effects: _____

Safety precautions: _____

_____

Name   Date

a Capitalization of Proper Nouns

✔ Specific buildings, cities, states, and public spaces are proper nouns and need to be capitalized.

Example: Old Post Office Tower; Arlington National Cemetery

■ Complete the chart by writing the proper nouns correctly.

Proper Nouns	Correct Capitalization
yellowstone national park	
central intelligence agency	
national wwII memorial	
tucson, arizona	
grand canyon national park	
the white house	
thomas jefferson memorial	
grand tetons national park	
oregon caves national monument	
portland, maine	
the great pyramid of giza	
the washington mall	
alcatraz island	
korean war veteran's memorial	
smithsonian institution	
gettysburg national cemetery	
grand canyon	
austin, texas	

ELD Standard
    Edit writing for basic conventions.
ELA Standard
    Use correct capitalization.

297

Name _____   Date _____

b Researching a Topic/Writing Captions

■ Research four monuments, parks, or historic buildings using an encyclopedia or online resources. Then draw them and provide a caption for each one.

ELD Standard
    Collect information from various sources.
ELA Standard
    Demonstrate the mechanics of writing and appropriate English usage.

Name _____   Date _____

ⓐ Past Tense with *Used to*

✔ The phrase *used to* indicates that an action took place over an extended period of time in the past. The simple form of the verb is combined with *used to*, as in the example below.

Example: I <u>used to sing</u> in the community chorus.

■ Read the sentences below. They are written in the present tense. Change the verb to the past tense, using *used to* + the simple tense of the verb.

1. We cross the George Washington Bridge every day on the way to work.

   _____

2. I visit the Vietnam Veterans' Memorial to pay tribute to the soldiers who died.

   _____

3. We ride the elevator to the top of the Empire State Building in New York City.

   _____

4. I take the walkway across the busy boulevard.

   _____

5. We take the train into the city to see our favorite musicians play.

   _____

6. My favorite New York City borough is the Bronx.

   _____

7. I fly in a blimp once a year.

   _____

8. I take my niece and nephew to Coney Island every summer.

   _____

9. My favorite building in New York is the Chrysler Building.

   _____

ELD Standard
    Edit writing for grammatical structures and the mechanics of writing.
ELA Standard
    Identify and use infinitives.

Name _____   Date _____

b Superlatives

▬▬ ▬▬ ▬▬ ▬▬ ▬▬ ▬▬ ▬▬ ▬▬ ▬▬ ▬▬ ▬▬ ▬▬ ▬▬ ▬▬ ▬▬

✔ When forming the superlative, you usually add *-est* to short adjectives, while longer adjectives are preceded by *the most*.

Example: The Empire State Building was <u>the tallest</u> building in the United States during the 1940s.

The bridges of New York are some of <u>the most beautiful</u> in the world.

▬▬ ▬▬ ▬▬ ▬▬ ▬▬ ▬▬ ▬▬ ▬▬ ▬▬ ▬▬ ▬▬ ▬▬ ▬▬ ▬▬ ▬▬

■ Use the facts from each box to write superlative sentences about the bridges.

> **The George Washington Bridge**, New York
>
> Over the Hudson River
>
> Building began in 1927 and the bridge opened to the public in 1931.
>
> Opened: (Upper deck) October 25, 1931
>
> Length: 4,760 feet
>
> Tower height: 604 feet
>
> Steel used: 43,000 tons

1. _____

2. _____

> **The Verrazano Narrows Bridge**, New York
>
> Over the Hudson River
>
> Building began in 1959 and the upper deck opened to the public in 1964. The lower deck opened to the public in 1969.
>
> Length: 6,690 feet
>
> Tower height: 693 feet
>
> Steel used: 127,000 tons

1. _____

2. _____

ELD Standard
    Edit writing for basic conventions.
ELA Standard
    Identify types and structure of sentences.

Brooklyn Bridge, New York

Over the East River

Building began in 1870 and bridge opened to the public in 1883.

Length: 3,456 feet

Tower height: 277 feet

Total length of cable used: 4,060 miles

1. _____

2. _____

Name _____ Date _____

a Tag Questions

━━━

✔ Short questions at the end of sentences that ask for a yes/no answer are called *tag questions*.

✔ If the main part of the sentence is negative, then the tag question is affirmative. If the main part of the sentence is affirmative, then the tag question is negative.

Examples: You are in seventh grade, aren't you?

You aren't taking algebra, are you?

The teacher walks to school every day, doesn't he?

The teacher doesn't walk to school every day, does he?

━━━

▪ Formulate questions using both negative and affirmative tag questions.

Example:

Pam is moving to Boston.

Pam is moving to Boston, isn't she? _____

Pam isn't moving to Boston, is she? _____

1. Raul rides the subway to work.

_____

_____

2. You get off the subway at the Quincy Center stop on the Red Line.

_____

_____

3. You prefer riding the subway to driving into Boston.

_____

_____

4. You get a transit pass each month.

_____

_____

ELD Standard
Use more complex vocabulary and sentences appropriate for language arts and other content areas.
ELA Standard
Identify types and structure of sentences.

5. The subway tracks are elevated in my neighborhood.

_____

_____

■ Write the appropriate tag question to complete each of the following questions.

1. Boston has the best subway system, _____?

2. My dad doesn't take the Blue Line, _____?

3. You don't ever take taxis, _____?

4. You used to ride the train to school, _____?

5. You didn't used to live in New York, _____?

Name   Date

b Writing Directions

■ Use the map to write directions for a tourist trying to get from one point to another on the Boston Subway system. Be sure to write using complete sentences.

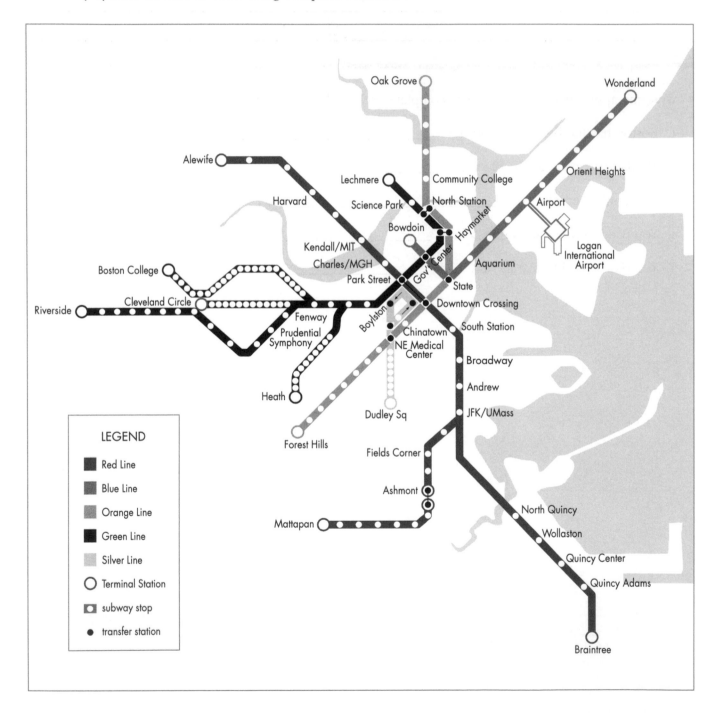

ELD Standard
Use more complex vocabulary and sentences appropriate for language arts and other content areas.
ELA Standard
Demonstrate the mechanics of writing and appropriate English usage.

1. How do you get from Oak Grove to Harvard?

   _____

   _____

   _____

   _____

2. How do you get from Braintree to Boston College?

   _____

   _____

   _____

   _____

3. How do you get from the Airport to Harvard?

   _____

   _____

   _____

   _____

4. How do you get from Bowdoin to Wonderland?

   _____

   _____

   _____

   _____

Name   Date
_____

a Nicknames for Cities

▬ ▬ ▬ ▬ ▬ ▬ ▬ ▬ ▬ ▬ ▬ ▬ ▬ ▬ ▬ ▬ ▬ ▬ ▬ ▬

■ Read the names in the column on the left-hand side of the page. Then draw a line to connect the name to the city it refers to. Use an encyclopedia or online resources if you need help.

The Athens of America	New York City
Garden City	Detroit
Birthplace of Baseball	Dallas
City of Angels	Budapest
The City of Brotherly Love	New Orleans
The City of Light	Cooperstown
The Eternal City	Cuernavaca
The Melting Pot	Jerusalem
Motor City	Paris
Tinsel town	Sacramento
Big D	Philadelphia
The Pearl of the Danube	Hollywood
The City of Eternal Spring	Rome
City of Peace	Pasadena
The Big Easy	Boston
Rose City	Savannah
River City	Los Angeles

ELD Standard
   Collect information from various sources.
ELA Standard
   Understand and explain the figurative and metaphorical use of words in context.

Name _____   Date _____

b Interjections and Exclamations

✔ Interjections and exclamations are sentences that show strong emotion.

Ah	Hey	Ouch	Wow	Incredible
Whoa	Aha	Hurray	Oh, dear	Please

■ Use each of the interjections listed above in a complete sentence. Be sure to use all the appropriate punctuation.

Example:

_____ Hurray! The Dodgers won yesterday! _____

1. _____

2. _____

3. _____

4. _____

5. _____

6. _____

7. _____

8. _____

9. _____

10. _____

■ Can you think of more interjections or exclamatory phrases? Write them in the boxes below.

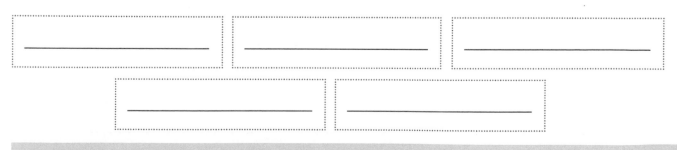

ELD Standard
  Revise one's writing for proper use of final punctuation, capitalization, and correct spelling.
ELA Standard
  Identify types and structure of sentences.

307

Name _____   Date _____

⟨a⟩ Capitalization of Proper Nouns

✔ The names of neighborhoods, districts, and parks are capitalized because they are proper nouns.

■ Write examples of the following categories. You might want to work with a partner or small group for this activity.

Parks

_____

_____

_____

_____

_____

Neighborhoods

_____

_____

_____

_____

_____

Districts

_____

_____

_____

_____

_____

■ Visit the library and research one of the examples that you wrote above. Then write an informative paragraph about it in the space below. Be sure to include descriptive adjectives to *paint a picture* of the place you are describing.

Name _____

_____

_____

_____

_____

_____

ELD Standard
   Edit writing for basic conventions.
ELA Standard
   Use correct capitalization.

Name   Date

b Possessive Apostrophes

✔ An apostrophe followed by *s* and placed at the end of a noun shows ownership.

Example: <u>Miami's</u> South Beach district is known for its architecture.

■ Read the sentences below and rewrite the possessive noun on the line, making sure to add the *'s* ending.

1. Miami South Beach district is beautiful! _____

2. Art Deco most popular period was pre-World War II. _____

3. The gallery is displaying Andy Warhol work. _____

4. South Beach is often referred to as America Riviera. _____

5. I took a look at the architect plans for the remodeling of the old home. _____

6. Patricia last name is Garcia-Moreno. _____

7. New York skyline changed drastically on September 11, 2001. _____

8. San Francisco Mission District is a lively, interesting neighborhood. _____

9. I wanted to visit the ghost town old school and jail. _____

10. The steamship lounge was as luxurious as anything she had ever seen before!

_____

■ Now write your own sentences using the possessive apostrophe. Use proper nouns in your sentences.

1. _____

2. _____

3. _____

4. _____

5. _____

ELD Standard
  Identify and use parts of speech.
ELA Standard
  Use apostrophe in the possessive case of nouns.

309

Name _____   Date _____

a Serial Commas

✔ A noun is a person, place, thing, or idea. When you list nouns in a series, use commas to separate them and use the conjunction *and* before the last noun.

Example: **New Orleans has music, food, and parties known around the world!**

■ Rewrite the following sentences, placing commas between the series of nouns.

1. The dancer singer and musician played in the club.

   _____

2. French language music and cuisine helped shaped the character of New Orleans.

   _____

3. I took a boat car and train all in the same day.

   _____

4. The carriage clothing and tools were all donated to the museum.

   _____

■ Write sentences combining the nouns and the verb indicated. Be sure to place the commas correctly between the series of nouns. The first one is already done.

1. **Nouns:** historic buildings, riverboats, restaurants; **verb:** explore

   You can explore historic buildings, riverboats, and restaurants in New Orleans.

2. **Nouns:** shrimp, oysters, crab; **verb:** prepare

   _____

3. **Nouns:** French Quarter, Lakeview, Riverbed; **verb:** visit

   _____

4. **Nouns:** mask, costume, beads, Mardi Gras; **verb:** wear

   _____

ELD Standard
   Edit and correct basic grammatical structures and usage of the conventions of writing.
ELA Standard
   Use commas for items in a series.

Name _____   Date _____

a Ordinal Numbers

━ ━

✔ Ordinal numbers express degree or sequence.

━ ━

■ Follow the directions by marking the correct ordinal number.

1. Mark the fifth milk carton with an **X**.

2. Circle the fourteenth carrot.

3. Color the ninth tomato red.

4. Underline the sixteenth palm tree.

5. Mark the eleventh strawberry with an **X**.

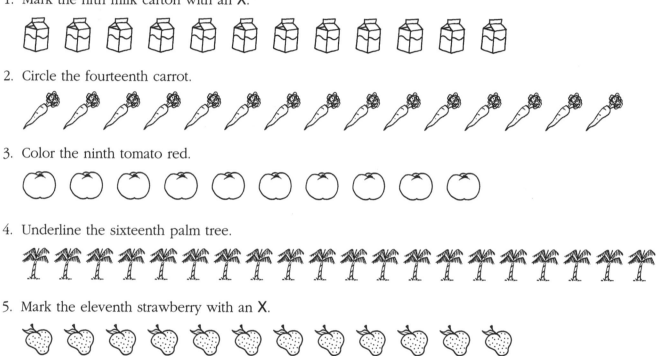

━ ━

■ Read the sentences and fill in the blanks with the correct ordinal number.

1. October is the _____ month of the year.

2. Independence Day is on the _____ of July.

3. A *quinceañera* is when Mexican girls celebrate their _____ birthday.

4. If there are seven days in a week, does that mean that Sunday is the _____ day or the first day?

5. I have been to Mexico ten times already. Next summer, I'm going for the

   _____ time.

ELD Standard
   Understand and follow simple written directions for classroom-related activities.
ELA Standard
   Identify and correctly use all parts of speech.

313

Name　　　　　　　　　　　　　　　　　　　Date

b Ranking Superlatives

■ Study the graph below about U.S. population statistics. Complete the sentences that follow with the appropriate ordinal number or state name. Take into consideration that the largest state refers to the one that has the most population, and the smallest one to the one that has the least. (These statistics include the District of Columbia.)

State	July 2003 Population	Population Rank, 2003	State	July 2003 Population	Population Rank, 2003
Alabama	4,500,752	23	Michigan	10,079,985	8
Alaska	648,818	47	Minnesota	5,059,375	21
Arizona	5,580,811	18	Mississippi	2,881,281	31
Arkansas	2,725,714	32	Missouri	5,704,484	17
California	35,484,453	1	Montana	917,621	44
Colorado	4,550,688	22	Nebraska	1,739,291	38
Connecticut	3,483,372	29	Nevada	2,241,154	35
Delaware	817,491	45	New Hampshire	1,287,687	41
District of Columbia	563,384	50	New Jersey	8,638,396	10
Florida	17,019,068	4	New Mexico	1,874,614	36
Georgia	8,684,715	9	New York	19,190,115	3
Hawaii	1,257,608	42	North Carolina	8,407,248	11
Idaho	1,366,332	39	North Dakota	633,837	48
Illinois	12,653,544	5	Ohio	11,435,798	7
Indiana	6,195,643	14	Oklahoma	3,511,532	28
Iowa	2,944,062	30	Oregon	3,559,596	27
Kansas	2,723,507	33	Pennsylvania	12,365,455	6
Kentucky	4,117,827	26	Rhode Island	1,076,164	43
Louisiana	4,496,334	24	South Carolina	4,147,152	25
Maine	1,305,728	40	South Dakota	764,309	46
Maryland	5,508,909	19	Tennessee	5,841,748	16
Massachusetts	6,433,422	13	Texas	22,118,509	2

ELD Standard
Identify basic vocabulary, mechanics, and sentence structure in a piece of writing.
ELA Standard
Locate information by using a variety of consumer, workplace, and public documents.

State	July 2003 Population	Population Rank, 2003
Utah	2,351,467	34
Vermont	619,107	49
Virginia	7,386,330	12
Washington	6,131,445	15
West Virginia	1,810,354	37
Wisconsin	5,472,299	20
Wyoming	501,242	51
Total US	**290,809,777**	

Source: U.S. Bureau of the Census. Web: www.census.gov.

1. Texas is the _____ largest state in the country.

2. Vermont is the _____ smallest state.

3. Illinois is the _____ largest state in the U.S.

4. _____ is the <u>fourth</u> largest state.

5. _____ is the <u>fifteenth</u> largest state.

6. _____ is the <u>twenty-ninth</u> largest state.

7. Virginia is the _____ largest state in the country.

8. New York is the _____ largest state.

9. North Dakota is the _____ smallest state in America.

10. Wisconsin is the _____ largest state.

Name _____   Date _____

a Habitual Past Tense using *Used to*

▬ ▬ ▬ ▬ ▬ ▬ ▬ ▬ ▬ ▬ ▬ ▬ ▬ ▬ ▬ ▬ ▬ ▬

✔ The habitual past tense of a verb is written with the simple present tense of the main verb preceded by *used to*. It tells about what was done in the past on a regular basis.

▬ ▬ ▬ ▬ ▬ ▬ ▬ ▬ ▬ ▬ ▬ ▬ ▬ ▬ ▬ ▬ ▬ ▬

■ Read the phrases below. Then write sentences incorporating the phrase and the habitual past tense with the words *used to*, as in the example.

Example:

go to the movies

My parents used to go to the movies every Saturday night.

1. sweep the sidewalk

_____

2. go to the La Brea Tar Pits

_____

3. paint murals

_____

4. collect fossils

_____

5. draw prehistoric animals

_____

6. jog on the beach

_____

7. visit famous landmarks

_____

8. study the Spanish heritage of Los Angeles

_____

ELD Standard
    Edit and correct basic grammatical structures and usage of the conventions of writing.
ELA Standard
    Identify types and structure of sentences.

■ Compose five of your own sentences using the words *used to*. Be sure to use correct punctuation.

1. _____

2. _____

3. _____

4. _____

5. _____

Name _____   Date _____

ⓑ Abbreviations of States

■ Connect the columns, drawing a line from the landmark name to its corresponding city. Then write the state abbreviation in the line that follows the city. Use a comma to separate the city and state abbreviation. You might want to use an encyclopedia or atlas to complete this activity.

Golden Gate Bridge	Chicago _____
Statue of Liberty	St. Louis _____
Sears Tower	New York _____
St. Louis Gateway Arch	San Francisco _____
Liberty Bell	Philadelphia _____
Old House Meeting House	Boston _____
U.S. Capitol	Washington _____
Susan B. Anthony House	Rochester _____
Brooklyn Bridge	Manhattan-Brooklyn _____
Mark Twain House	Hartford _____
Kennedy Space Center	Cape Canaveral _____
Space Needle	Seattle _____

ELD Standard
    Recognize common abbreviations.
ELA Standard
    Recognize common abbreviations.

Name _____   Date _____

a Adjectives Together in Sentences

✔ When two adjectives of the same kind are used together in a sentence, they are separated by a comma.

Example: The <u>bright, colorful</u> streets of Chinatown are fascinating!

(*Bright* and *colorful* are adjectives that both describe physical characteristics.)

■ Write facts about the following cities using the prompts listed, as in the example.

Example:

Adjectives: foggy, chilly; **noun:** Oregon coastline

I love visiting the foggy, chilly Oregon coastline. _____

1. **Adjectives:** speedy, modern; **noun:** subway

_____

2. **Adjectives:** breezy, warm; **noun:** beach

_____

3. **Adjectives:** isolated, wild; **noun:** island

_____

4. **Adjectives:** old, historic; **noun:** cable car

_____

5. **Adjectives:** magnificent, proud; **noun:** landmark

_____

6. **Adjectives:** tall, red; **noun:** bridge

_____

7. **Adjectives:** magnificent, shimmering; **noun:** skyline

_____

8. **Adjectives:** graceful, elegant; **noun:** pagoda

_____

ELD Standard
     Edit and correct basic grammatical structures and usage of the conventions of writing.
ELA Standard
     Use commas for items in a series.

319

■ Place a comma in the appropriate place in each sentence below.

1. I quickly put the drab uninteresting book back on the library shelf.

2. Did you struggle through the long difficult exam?

3. Every afternoon I hold my little purring kitten.

4. The confused embarrassed actor walked offstage after forgetting his lines.

5. Hand me that adorable sleepy puppy!

Name _____   Date _____

b Writing with Descriptive Words

━━ ━ ━━ ━━ ━━ ━━ ━━ ━━ ━━ ━━ ━━ ━━ ━━ ━━ ━━ ━━ ━━

✔ When you write using descriptive words, you use as many *colorful* adjectives as possible. Separate them with commas, whenever necessary.

━━ ━ ━━ ━━ ━━ ━━ ━━ ━━ ━━ ━━ ━━ ━━ ━━ ━━ ━━ ━━ ━━

▪ Select two of the topics listed in the box below. Write one-paragraph descriptions of them, using interesting adjectives and correct punctuation. Use an encyclopedia to research the topics.

Alcatraz Island	U.S. Mint (San Francisco)
Angel Island	Golden Gate Park
San Francisco cable cars	San Francisco Art Institute
Fort Point	Spreckels Mansion

Topic: _____

_____

_____

_____

_____

_____

Topic: _____

_____

_____

_____

_____

_____

ELD Standard
Identify and use parts of speech.
ELA Standard
Use commas for items in a series.

Name   Date

a Spelling of Numbers

✔ There are certain rules to follow regarding whether to write out numbers or not.

1. The numbers *zero* through *nine* are usually spelled out.

2. All numbers 10 and larger are usually written as numerals.

3. Very large numbers that can be written as two words are spelled out. Example: *Three million.*

4. Large numbers containing decimals can combine words and numerals. Example: *2.6 billion.*

5. If a sentence begins with a number, the number is spelled out.

■ Which is the best way to write the following numbers? Mark the correct answers below and write them in the spaces provided.

1. _____ windsurfers were out in the bay during the storm.
   - ☐ 3
   - ☐ Three

2. I discovered that the city has

   _____ people.
   - ☐ two.one million
   - ☐ 2.one million
   - ☐ 2.1 million
   - ☐ two point one million

3. There were _____ cello players in the school orchestra.
   - ☐ two
   - ☐ 2

4. There are over _____
   people in the world.
   - ☐ 6,000,000,000
   - ☐ six billion
   - ☐ 6 billion

5. Pablo got _____ out of _____ on the Algebra test.
   - ☐ 9, 10
   - ☐ nine, ten
   - ☐ nine, 10
   - ☐ 9, ten

6. We'll invite _____ family members to our Thanksgiving dinner.
   - ☐ sixteen
   - ☐ 16

7. The company was

   $_____ in debt by last year.
   - ☐ 3.9,000,000
   - ☐ three.nine million
   - ☐ 3.9 million
   - ☐ three point nine million

8. _____ boys tried out for the soccer team, and _____ of them made it.
   - ☐ 7, 6
   - ☐ 7, six
   - ☐ Seven, 6
   - ☐ Seven, six

ELD Standard
Produce independent writing with consistent use of capitalization and periods, and correct spelling.
ELA Standard
Recognize and use knowledge of spelling patterns.

Name _____   Date _____

b Vocabulary/Writing an Essay

▪ Read the names of the countries below. Select one and research it in the library or online. You may also research another country of your choice. Then, following the Writing Checklist, write a three-paragraph essay on the country you selected. Use almanacs, encyclopedias, atlases, and other references to find in-depth, current information.

Ireland	Slovakia	Georgia	Canada	Chile
New Zealand	Brazil	France	Vietnam	Korea
Japan	Costa Rica	Switzerland	Venezuela	

Country: _____

_____

_____

_____

_____

_____

_____

_____

_____

_____

_____

_____

_____

_____

_____

_____

_____

ELD Standard
  Collect information from various sources and take notes on a given topic.
ELA Standard
  Include evidence compiled thorough the formal research process.

Writing Checklist / Peer Editing

Previewing: Things to do before writing
Choose a topic. Write a sentence that clearly states your theme.
Brainstorm ideas. Create a list, outline, table, graph, diagram, story map, mind map, or other graphic organizer.
Gather data. Research the Internet, take notes from secondary sources, create surveys, and interview primary sources.
Organize your original ideas and notes from your sources.

Drafting: The first version of your work
Choose and sequence your ideas. Use your graphic organizers, data, and notes.
Prepare visuals, such as charts, maps, and graphs.
Decide your point of view: first person, third person, etc. Predict what your readers expect.
Write a first draft.

Revising: Improving your work	Examples
Read over what you wrote. Does it make sense? Do words, phrases, sentences, or paragraphs need to be added or taken out?	
Make sure each sentence has a subject (with the main person, place, thing, idea).	The Iroquois lived in New York's Finger Lakes region. (Incorrect: *lived in New York's Finger Lakes region.*)
Make sure each sentence has a predicate (which contains a verb, or action word).	Sequoyah invented the Cherokee syllabary. (Incorrect: *Sequoyah the Cherokee syllabary.*)
When using the present tense, make sure the noun and verb agree in number. The general rule is: If the subject is plural, the verb can't end in -s.	Abigail Adams boycotts British tea. Everyday except Sundays, The Daughters of Liberty sew colorful blankets. (Incorrect: *Abigail Adams boycott British tea. The Daughters of Liberty sews colorful blankets.*)
Check your past tense verbs. If it's a regular verb, make sure it ends in -ed. If it's irregular, use the correct form.	William Dawes and Paul Revere prepared to warn the colonists. They rode quickly toward Lexington.
Use plurals correctly.	poems, speeches, chambers of government, (incorrect: *chamber of governments*), spies (incorrect: *spys*), alumnae, alumni
Use correct parts of speech (adverbs, adjectives, etc.)	The brave British troops neatly dressed in their bright red uniforms marched dejectedly out of Yorktown.
Use the most precise, colorful, appropriate words possible.	Eli Whitney's invention, the cotton gin was very practical because it made separating seeds from the cotton a lot easier and faster. (Instead of: *Eli Whitney's invention, the cotton gin, was very good because …*)
Expressions and idioms are not changed.	Samuel Fulton's business was in the black. The steamship helped the business earn more money.
Use sufficient supporting sentences to make your point.	Thomas Jefferson was a popular leader, but not everyone liked his ideas. Alexander Hamilton, for example, believed that the upper class should lead the country. Antislavery groups also opposed Jefferson.
Use transition words to connect separate ideas.	furthermore, however, henceforth, in conclusion, on the other hand, etc.

Proofreading: Correcting spelling, punctuation, and grammatical errors

If you typed your work on a word processor or computer, run a spell-check.
Always capitalize the word *I*.
Check to see that each sentence, question, and exclamation begins with a capital letter.
Capitalize the first letter in the days of the week, the months of the year, book and magazine titles, as well as the names of people and places.
Check to see that each sentence ends with the correct punctuation: ■ A period ends a statement. (.) ■ A question mark ends a question. (?) ■ An exclamation point ends a sentence that expresses strong emotion. (!)
Check to see that each new idea begins a new paragraph. Indent each new paragraph. If your writing has more than one paragraph, you can indent each new paragraph or skip a line between each paragraph.
Check the spelling of frequently misspelled words such as *their, they're, there; two, to, too; its, it's*.
Check the spelling of contractions.
Make sure that commas are used correctly. ■ Use a comma between the name of a city and a state, a province, or a colony. ■ Use a comma between the day and the year in a date. ■ Use a comma to separate three or more items in a series.

Publishing: Presenting your work to the world

Have a partner edit your story using this Writing Checklist.
Copy over your story neatly. Write it on a clean sheet of paper, or type it on a typewriter, word processor, or computer.
Insert your graphics.
Publish it in print or on your personal web page.
Read your final story to a partner, to the class, or to someone at home.